Foreword

Dear Customer,

Welcome to this publication, the follow up to
our hugely successful ' Homes For Life'. Once
again we offer a wealth of styles, together
with great attention to detail both internally
and externally. All designs may be
incorporated into a rural or an urban setting,
with changes to finishes as necessary to suit
and blend in with the surrounding landscape
(these are carried out free of charge by our
office).

Once again you can order plans directly from our office or alternatively
through our web site at www.houseplans.ie. Many people alter the layout of
plans to some degree and for a quote on this you may contact us by phone or
email and we shall respond immediately. In the vast majority of cases no
charge or a small fee is incurred. Where the changes are more extensive a
draft is verified by you prior to completion of the planning and construction
drawings, after payment of a 50% deposit.

We can also apply for planning permission on your behalf, upon provision of a
number of items from you, most importantly scaled ordnance survey maps
showing the proposed site with any noteworthy features (such as neighbouring
dwellings) in the vicinity. We find from experience that while most planning
permission rules, regulations and documents are uniform throughout Ireland,
each individual Authority have their own particular idiosyncrasies and
requirements. Our office which was established in the mid 90s has great
experience in this field. Our helpful and qualified staff shall be delighted to
answer any queries you may have in relation to ordering, finishes etc. and we
look forward to helping you achieve your goal of a house and home, as we
have done for thousands of others.

Mark Kelly M.A.S.I., M.R.I.C.S.

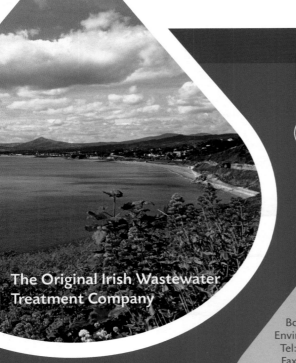

ACKNOWLEDGMENTS

Designs:
All designs by Mark Kelly,
Corporate Member Architecture &
Surveying Institute.

Computer Graphics:
AH Art, Tramore, Co. Waterford

Printing by:
Kilkenny People Printing Limited.

Editorial:
Landscaping by Ann Marie Mahon.
Interior Design by Michelle Burke.
Mortgage tips by BOI Finance

PUBLISHER

MK Home Design Limited.
22 Upper Patrick Street, Kilkenny,
Ireland.

ACKNOWLEDGMENTS

Mary Kelly, Maria Donnelly,
Jason Barry, Trevor Minchin

MK Home Design Ltd.
Dream Houseplans

CONTENTS

As a general guide to room layouts throughout this publication the reader will find that:

- Entrance/Landing areas - brown
- Kitchen/Dining areas - green
- Living/Sitting areas - blue
- Study/Office areas - magenta
- Bedrooms - red
- Bathrooms/en-suite/w.c areas - yellow
- Sun room/conservatory areas - orange
- Garage/Utility/HP areas - grey

As warm as

Section A

House Designs up to 1350 sq. ft

TIP: If your house is to be finished in natural stone, then extra wide foundations shall probably be required, so have this decision made well in advance of commencement. For reconstituted stone this normally does not apply. If in doubt early on, then widen the foundations.

HOUSE A-201

A simple touch such as a splayed sunroom to the side provides an elegant addition to a bungalow such as this. The fact that there is no ensuite to the master bedroom allows the main bathroom to become larger and more spacious. Brick often combines very well with red roof tiles as shown in this image.

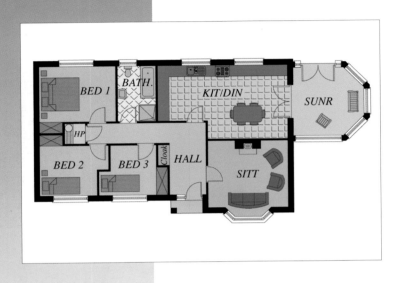

A-201		
Hallway	1.9m	6'2"
Sitting Room	4.2 x 3.6m	13' 8" x 11' 8"
Sun Room	3.7 x 3.7m	12' 1" x 12'1
Kitchen/Dining	6.7 x 3.9m	21'10" x 12'7
Bedroom 1	4.0 x 3.0m	13' 1" x 9' 8
Bedroom 2	3.6 x 2.7m	11' 8" x 8'6"
Bedroom 3	3.6 x 3.1m	11'8" x 10'2"
Bathroom	2.0 x 3.0m	6'6" x 9'8
Hot Press	1.1 x 1.1m	3'7" x 3'7
FRONTAGE	13.6m	45 ft
AREA	108.2 sq. m.	1164 sq. ft.

See page 104 to order this design by Post

HOUSE **A-202**

An enticing, compact single storey residence. This house can be very economical to build yet highly attractive in appearance. This type of design is highly favourable with planning authorities due to its 'indigenous' style.

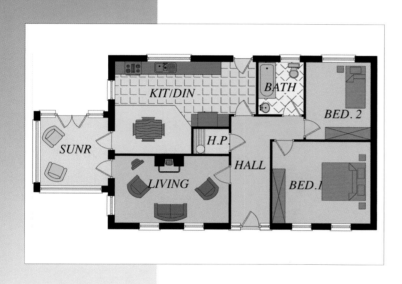

A-202		
Hallway	1.8m	5'9"
Living Room	5.2 x 3.2m	21' 3" x 14' 4"
Sun Room	3.3 x 3.1m	17' 1" x10' 5"
Kitchen/Dining	6.5 x 4.4m	21' 3" x 14' 4"
Bedroom 1	4.5 x 3.9m	14'4" x 12' 8"
Bedroom 2	3.7 x 3.0m	12' 1" x 9' 8"
Bathroom	2.5 x 2.1m	8' 2" x 6'9"
Hot Press	1.6 x 1.2m	5'.2" x 3'9"
FRONTAGE	12.4m	41 ft
AREA	103.6 sq. m.	1115 sq. ft.

See page 101 for plan prices

HOUSE A-203

A very popular type of house design. All space in this superb bungalow is used to full effect and maximum efficiency. The two bay windows on the front elevation offer great character to a relatively short façade.

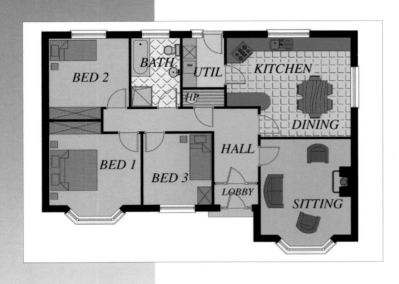

A-203		
Hallway	1.9m	6'2"
Lobby	1.9 x 1.0m	6'2" x 3'3"
Sitting room	4.2 x 3.9m	13'8" x 12'8"
Kitchen/Dining	5.3 x 4.4m	17'4" x 14'4"
Utility	2.2 x 1.8m	7'2" x 5'8"
Bedroom 1	3.7 x 3.9m	12'1" x 12'8"
Bedroom 2	3.4 x 3.6m	11'2" x 11'8"
Bedroom 3	3.1 x 2.9m	10'2" x 9'5"
Bathroom	3.0 x 2.1m	9'8" x 6'9"
Hot Press	1.8 x 0.8m	5'11" x 2'6
FRONTAGE	13.6m	45 ft
AREA	103.5 sq. m.	1114 sq. ft.

HOUSE A-204

A nice dormer dwelling full of character. The internal layout is both practical and spacious at the same time. This design offers many good-sized rooms in a relatively small space. The large utility room incorporates a copper cylinder.

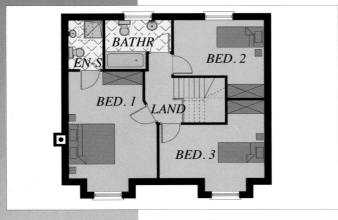

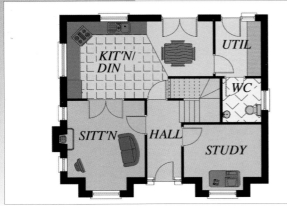

A-204		
Hallway	3.5 x 1.5m	11'5" x 4'9"
Sitting Room	3.5 x 3.4m	11'5" x 11'1"
Study	3.4 x 2.4m	11'5" x 7'9"
Kitchen	6.4 x 3.5m	20'10"x 11'5"
Utility	2.5 x 2.0m	8'2" x 6'6"
WC	2.0 x 1.7m	6' 6" x 5'6"
Bedroom 1	4.8 x 3.8m	15'7" x 12'6"
En suite	2.2 x 1.5m	7'2" x 4'9"
Bedroom 2	3.9 x 2.5m	12'8" x 8'2"
Bedroom 3	4.6 x 2.4m	15'1" x 7'9"
Bathroom	2.9 x 2.2m	9'5" x 7'2"
Landing	3.0 x 1.2m	9'8" x 3'9"
FRONTAGE	9.1m	30 ft
AREA	122.6 sq. m .	1319 sq. ft.

HOUSE A-205

A tremendously versatile house type. The relatively wide roof is perfect for later conversion of the attic space if desired. It is intended that the double doors from the dining area lead out on to a future patio.

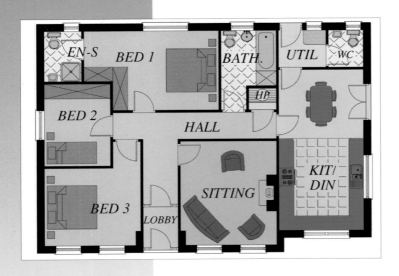

A-205		
Lobby	1.7 x 1.4m	5'8" x 4'6"
Hall	1.4	4'6"
Sitting Room	4.3 x 3.8m	14'1" x 12'5"
Kitchen/Dining	6.6 x 3.4m	21'6" x 11'2"
Utility	1.9 x 1.6m	6'2" x 5'2"
WC	1.5 x 1.4m	4'9" x 4'6"
Hot Press	1.1 x 0.9m	3'6" x 2'10"
Bathroom	3.3 x 2.2m	10'.8" x 7'2"
Bedroom 1	5.4 x 3.3m	17'7" x 10'8"
En suite	2.1 x 1.5m	6'9" x 4'9"
Bedroom 2	3.4 x 2.6m	11'2" x 8'5"
Bedroom 3	3.8 x 3.2m	12'5" x 10'5"
FRONTAGE	13.4m	44 ft
AREA	110.8 sq. m.	1192 sq. ft.

HOUSE A-206

This superb spacious residence has it all. The storage space available, both in the utility and hot press is larger than normal. All rooms have ample window space giving valuable light to these areas.

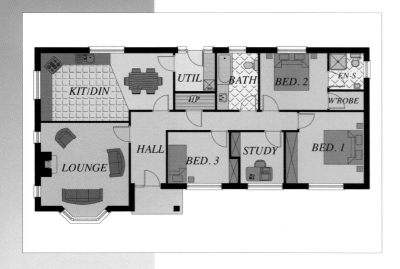

A-206		
Hall	1.8m	5'9"
Lounge	4.6 x 4.4m	15'1" x 14'4"
Kitchen/Dining	6.9 x 3.6m	22'6" x 11'8"
Utility	2.1 x 2.0m	6'9" x 6'6"
Hot Press	2.0 x 0.9m	6'6" x 2'10"
Bathroom	3.0 x 2.1m	9'8" x 6'9"
Bedroom 1	4.0 x 3.8m	13'1" x 12'5"
Bedroom 2	3.3 x 3.1m	10'8" x 10'2"
En suite	1.2 x 1.9m	6'2" x 6'2"
Wardrobe	1.9 x 1.0m	6'2" x 3'3"
Study	2.7 x 2.7m	8'9" x 8'9"
Bedroom 3	3.1 x 2.7m	10'2" x 8'9"
FRONTAGE	17.4m	57 ft
AREA	123.6 sq. m.	1330 sq. ft.

See page 104 to order this design by Post

HOUSE A-207

A deceptively spacious bungalow. A lounge area separate from the main sitting room has always been popular as a method of keeping a 'good room'. The square shaped kitchen dining area is at the same time both practical and attractive.

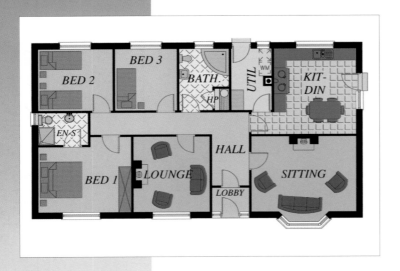

A-207		
Entrance Lobby	1.8 x 1.2m	5'9" x 3'9"
Hall	1.8m	5'9"
Sitting Room	5.0 x 3.7m	16'4" x 12'1"
Kitchen/Dining	4.3 x 4.0m	14'1" x 13'1"
Utility	3.1 x 1.9m	10'2" x 6'2"
Lounge	3.7 x 3.7m	12'1" x 12'1"
Bedroom 1	4.4 x 3.8m	14'4" x 12'5"
En Suite	2.4 x 1.6m	7'9" x 5'2"
Bedroom 2	3.6 x 3.1m	11'8" x 10'2"
Bedroom 3	3.1 x 3.0m	10'2" x 9'8"
Bathroom	3.1 x 2.4m	10'2" x 7'9"
Hot Press	1.1 x 0.7m	3'6" x 2'4"
FRONTAGE	15.9m	52 ft
AREA	125.3 sq. m.	1349 sq. ft.

See page 101 for plan prices

HOUSE A-208

You can see why this type of three-bedroom layout is very popular. The unusual corner window on the dining room adds a nice feature to this area. The hot press and copper cylinder within the bathroom save both space and cost to this area.

A-208		
Hall	1.2m	3'9"
Dining Room	3.7 x 3.6m	12'1" x 11'8"
Kitchen	3.8 x 3.6m	12'5" x 11'8"
Sitting Room	3.9 x 3.6m	12'8" x 11'8"
Bedroom 1	3.6 x 3.3m	11'8" x 10'8"
En suite	2.1 x 0.9m	6'9" x 2'10"
Bedroom 2	3.6 x 3.0m	11'8" x 9'8"
Bedroom 3	3.0 x 3.0m	9'8" x 9'8"
Bathroom	3.0 x 1.8m	9'8" x 5'9"
FRONTAGE	13.1m	43 ft
AREA	96.6 sq. m.	1040 sq. ft.

HOUSE A-209

The welcoming two-storey has a simple yet highly elegant exterior. The fabulous lounge area, which goes right from front to back offers tremendous space and comfort. Due to its straight lines and relatively simple roof this attractive dwelling can be very cost effective to build.

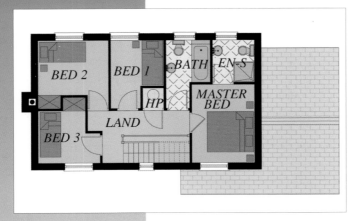

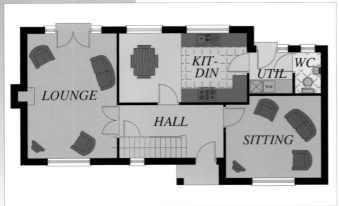

A-209		
Entrance Hall	4.4 x 2.3m	14'4" x 7' 5"
Sitting Room	4.0 x 3.6m	13'1" x 11'8"
Lounge	5.4 x 3.8m	17'7" x 12'5"
Kitchen /Dining	5.4 x 3.0m	17'7" x 9'8"
Utility	2.0 x 1.8m	6'5" x 5'9"
WC	1.8 x 0.9m	5'9" x 2'10"
Landing	2.3 x 3.7m	7'5" x 12'1"
Master Bedroom	3.5 x 2.7m	11'5" x 8'9"
En suite	1.9 x 1.8m	6'2" x 5'9"
Bathroom	3.0 x 1.9m	9'8" x 6'2"
Bedroom 1	3.0 x 2.3m	9'8" x 7'5"
Bedroom 2	3.0 x 3.0m	9'8" x 9' 8"
Bedroom 3	2.6 x 2.3m	8'5" x 7'5"
Hot Press	0.9 x 0.9m	2'10" x 2'10"
FRONTAGE	13.0m	43 ft
AREA	120.5 sq. m.	1297 sq. ft.

Interior Design

Introduction

Interior design is a term widely used today with the advent and popularity of so many television programmes and magazines endeavouring to cover the subject. Whether it conjures up images of pleasant pastimes designing and decorating or of more serious DIY disasters, it is something which cannot be avoided if building or refurbishing a home, office or business.

Many will have a natural flair for designing a scheme while others may need to call in a professional Interior Designer to help coordinate it all together. Either way, there are a number of key areas which must be addressed long before any actual decorating takes place and these are outlined in this dedicated Interiors section.

Planning the Space

This is the most critical part to the success of any scheme, but often the most frustrating and tedious as it requires patience and careful thought before diving into the "real " decorating. Good planning is necessary whether building from scratch or simply choosing a piece of furniture for a room. The main function of the room is the primary element to consider, whether it is to be a TV room or kids playroom or perhaps both, who will be predominantly using the room and at what times of the day? Will it always be a "playroom" and if not provision for changes in the future should be thought through now. Will there ever be more furniture needed than at present, or are there pets or the elderly to consider? These are just a sample of questions that should be asked and answered before delving any further into the project.

When purchasing furniture for a room, always take a tape measure with you or record the dimensions of the pieces and check with your room size before you buy. Cut out templates of the furniture from old newspaper and place them on the floor, then see can you actually walk around the room in comfort or reach the coffee table etc. Only then should a decision to buy be made. In addition, make sure that it will fit through the front door or up the stairs at home!

The spaces that we live in are becoming smaller and increasingly compact due to high demands for housing on limited available land. Therefore, getting the best use of the interior space is fundamental. Furniture design has recognised these issues with multi functional pieces being created to do many jobs within a small area ie encompassing practical storage solutions within dining tables and so on.. However, nothing can replace the human eye or common sense for thinking it through before you buy or build.

Proportion and Scale

These are very important elements when designing an interior scheme. It can often be difficult to know what will look "right" in a room and this is generally down to scale and size. Small furniture and under sized pictures / paintings will just look lost in a large scale room however, the most common mistake is the squashing together of over sized furniture within a smaller room making the proportions of everything look ridiculous. Sometimes an over sized picture can work well on a limited wall space but it is very much dependent on the type of house or room and the décor. Very ornate , detailed window dressings on a small scale window will dominate and look out of proportion to the rest of the room, while similarly one small photograph in a big expanse of wall will clearly be wrong.

Room Aspect

The direction a room faces and how much natural light and direct sunlight it receives is paramount to any interior scheme. A warm room will receive sunlight throughout most of the day and so is much more flexible in terms of colours schemes available. "Cold" rooms are generally north facing, getting little sun or even natural day light and so need careful consideration when choosing a colour scheme that will bring out the best the room has to offer. Use a compass to find out the direction, or simply observe at different times of the day to get the "feel" of each room.

Lighting

Light can be the most effective decorating tool in any interior, but all too often it is the least planned and last thought of element within a scheme. Lighting is paramount in creating the right feel in a room, altering the apparent size of a room while enhancing unusual features or artwork for display.

Lighting schemes should be planned right from the start of any project so that rewiring can be done with minimal disruption to the décor.

Natural daylight is ideal but can subject an interior to subtle changes throughout the day as the quality deteriorates. In addition, only 1% of natural light in an average room will reach areas farthest from the window. Therefore, artificial light is needed to discreetly boost natural daylight.

There are three types of lighting used within interiors, with a balanced combination of all three ideal in any room.

• General Lighting

General lighting should achieve an all round level of light to compliment natural daylight. Traditionally, a single central fitting provided the main light in many residential rooms. However, with good design and planning a wide variety of light fittings are now being used, not only adding decorative features to a room, but also creating a more distinctive aspect of overall lighting to interiors.

• Task Lighting

This is used to light specific functions within a room. It covers study areas, computer work stations, kitchen work areas, reading corners, inside wardrobes/cupboards and more. Adjustable fittings with flexibility of positioning are of key importance to the success of task lighting schemes.

• Accent Lighting

Accent lighting is used to add interest and drama to artwork, objects, sculptures, or special architectural features in an interior. It is also usually the lighting that provides the atmosphere within the room. Particular emphasis on accent lighting in planning can create a scheme that can really impress, and often for very little cost.

Colour Schemes

Colour is probably the most useful and versatile decorating tool available when designing a new scheme. It is by far the cheapest and most influential way to dramatically alter a space, often by simply painting a single wall. What colour shall I use? is usually the first question asked by all inspired decorators. However, there are many fundamental issues which must first be dealt with before finalising a colour scheme.

The space and size of a room or building must be carefully considered as indeed should the function. A room used by children and pets may not suit an all white/cream interior! The size of the area to be decorated must be considered as different colour palettes can create the illusion of space and light, or close in a room which may be unwelcomingly big. The direction or aspect of the room is very often overlooked, but it is key to a successful scheme. North and south facing rooms will have very different qualities of light with resulting atmospheres within a room. The amount and quality of natural light is absolutely critical as it will be the deciding factor in the final colours chosen. Light can either bring colour to life or deaden / flatten it completely, so the quality and quantity of both natural and artificial light is crucial.

A new colour scheme should always be tested under various light regimes at differing times of the day to get a real feel for the colour. Painting / papering a board and leaving it in the room, night and day and on different walls will put the new colour to the test. It is also important to work with the character of the room or building rather than force a colour upon it. Whilst heritage colours may be enjoying a revival, they would look out of place in an ultra modern, minimalist apartment block.

Inspiration for a colour scheme may come from anywhere, be it nature, a painting or sunset or a piece of fabric. The important thing to remember is that it is the combination of colours that will allow function.

A colour wheel can be split into two sections, warm and cold colours with a line drawn from the yellows to the purples. The reds, yellows and oranges are the warm colours whilst the

blues, greens and violets are the cooler shades. Warm colours tend to be used in rooms which are cold and lack natural light while the cooler shades work very well in bright, sunny rooms. Some of the cooler colours can be made warmer by adding undertones of a warmer colour to them, ie a blue with a hint of red will be warmer than a blue with green added. Warm colours can create the illusion of advancing walls or ceilings while cool colours tend to open up small spaces and appear to have a receding effect.

The atmosphere of a room will be dictated to a tremendous extent by the colour scheme chosen, be it warm or cold. Indeed, scientific research has proven that a person blindfolded can accurately identify a warm or cold colour simply by being in the room and touching the walls! However, the colour of a room can have a far greater influence than just merely transforming a space. The psychology of colour, ie the effect upon a person's mood is a fascinating area of interior design and an integral aspect of designing colour schemes for projects. Certain colours can calm the mind while others stimulate activity.

Fabrics

When choosing a colour scheme for a room, this is very often the most successful place to start! Matching a colour to a fantastic fabric is far easier than trying to find a fabric that will blend with a certain colour chosen. Fabric is the most sumptuous and rewarding way to make any room look incredible. There are simply hundreds of different types and styles of fabric to choose from but all consist of a type of fibre which has undergone a particular processes before being spun into yarn. In addition, styles of fabrics go in and out of fashion just as in the clothing industry, with seasonal trends following that seen on the catwalk, so what may be in vogue in the fashion world today will most certainly hit the interiors market shortly afterwards.

Natural fibres can be both animal and vegetable. Animal fibres include wool, mohair and silk and are all naturally flameproof, warm and resilient but are the most expensive to produce. Wool is very strong and copes well with wear and tear and so is used for carpeting and in upholstery fabrics. Silk is produced from the silk worm and although soft to the touch it is very strong. It is versatile and comes in a range of colours as it takes dye very well. It is available as taffetas, dupions, voiles and in all different weights, however it is prone to fading in the sunlight so needs to be treated with care.

Vegetable fibres such as cotton, linen and jute are the most common and are often found mixed along with other fibres. Linen is a strong natural fibre that comes in very fine through to coarser weaves. While it is resistant to dirt and wear and tear it does tend to crease and is usually better in a mix or linen union than on its own. Cotton is also soft to touch, but varies greatly in quality depending on the source of the fibre. It is available in a huge range of weaves, colours, designs and finishes from fine voiles to heavy calico and velvet. It is usually washable but may be prone to shrinking.

Manmade or synthetic fibres are hard wearing, easy to clean and do not fade but if used on their own they can be harsh and do not "breath", so they work best when combined with a natural fibre.

Viscose and acetate are both types of Rayon and they can be processed and woven to imitate the look of practically any type of fibre. Viscose which is the stronger of the two is often used for upholstery fabrics while acetate is lighter and can resemble silk and is only suitable for window treatments.

Polyester is extremely strong and is often added to other fibres to help them retain their shape and make them easier to care for. It can resemble silk very well.

Acrilan is a strong , soft woolly fibre which is easily cleaned and shrink resistant.

Nylon is resistant to abrasion and therefore added to other fibres for use in upholstery and carpets

Wall coverings

The walls and ceilings are the largest part of any decorating scheme, and although they will not form the most expensive area to decorate, they will have a dramatic influence on the success of a scheme. The covering on the walls will create the atmosphere and mood of the room , but can also have a big impact on the apparent size and proportions of the room. There are many options to consider when deciding on what to put on the walls including paint, wall paper, tiles, wood panelling or specialist plasterwork. Whatever option is chosen, preparation is the critical element to getting it right.

Paint is a very versatile medium with a huge range of available colours and the possibility of mixing to create new shades to match existing fabrics. In recent years paints have been used in very clever ways with special effects to create finishes such as ragging, colour washing etc. Many of these special paint effects can be done by anyone but some of them require considerable practice and the right equipment to achieve the proper effect.

Wallpaper is really coming back into vogue and with imaginative use can totally transform a room for little cost. Wallpaper is versatile in that it can be quick to set a mood, and the new paste varieties make it easier than ever to hang. It is also very useful for disguising flawed or uneven walls as is panelling the walls with wood left in its natural state or painted to suit a scheme.

Marmorino plasterwork is creating huge ripples in the design world where the old fashioned Italian and Spanish methods of finishing the walls in relative rough textured finish is now all the craze. There is a very special technique to this effect and the recipe for the Marmorino is a highly sought after secret. The workmen are especially trained to plaster this look effectively and it is not cheap. However, different dyes can be added into the plaster and also various prints and designs put onto the plasterwork to achieve a very individual look.

Floor Coverings

The type of flooring chosen will anchor a scheme together, however it must be practical. When planning a floor in a room never consider it in isolation. Doorways are usually left open and so the floor types within a space or house should have a harmonious flow between rooms. Before deciding on what to do with the floor, have a good look at what is already there. It may be possible to improve the existing floor, if it is wooden by sanding and re varnishing or even by adding a few coats of floor paint. Similarly, a tiled floor could be updated by re grouting and replacing old or worn tiles. A concrete floor could be painted using particular concrete paint or a special method which will dramatically change the look of the concrete. Lino floors can also be painted with wonderful success using some of the painting techniques suitable for walls.

Carpets are now mainly used in bedrooms providing a soft, warm environment underfoot. Tiles have become extremely popular, particularly in hallways as they are hard wearing and durable but be aware that they can be cold. Wooden floors still remain a popular choice with the wider plank varieties now taking precedence.

Accessories and Styling

When designing a room or a scheme it is often the small finishing touches that will really make the room and pull the whole scheme together. Little things can make a big difference and the key to getting a room "right" is to have the right accessories in the right place. Accessories can range from pictures, photographs, vases, flowers, clocks and sculptures to books and magazines. The clever trick to accessorizing successfully is to group similar objects together to create themes. A number of pictures or prints in similar type (themed) frames ie all wood or all chrome, grouped together on a wall, will make a much bigger statement than scattering them around the room. Photographs and mementos should be treated in the same way with a collection grouped together making a real impact. Look at the room sets of interior design magazines where this approach with accessories is always used to very subtle effect.

However, the danger with accessories is not to get carried away. Very often less is more, with a few striking pieces achieving more than an over crowded room fit for a car boot sale. Do not be afraid to criticise the room and "edit" things. This means taking a real look with a fresh eye at things you may not really like (perhaps they were gifts) or at objects that just fill a space but do not really match the scheme. Try removing them for a week and see if you can live without them. A room should only contain possessions that you like.

By Michelle Burke, Interior Designer, Rhodec International.
Tel 056 7767216; Mobile 086 3899104
e-mail burkemichelle@eircom.net

Section B

House Designs from 1351 sq. ft. up to 1650 sq. ft.

TIP: When making a planning application, if you have connections to the area, attach a letter outlining this as part of the application. List items such as; relatives close to the site (state distance), schools attended, sport club memberships etc. Never assume the area planner will take this for granted. See page 95.

HOUSE B-201

A superb single storey. A simple L-shape such as this gives great character to a relatively small dwelling. The extensive bathroom can easily accommodate both a large bath and a shower unit.

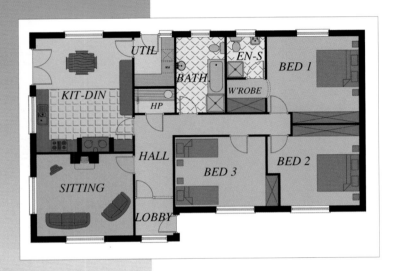

B-201		
Lobby	1.8 x 1.8m	5'9" x 5'9"
Hall	1.8m	5'9"
Sitting Room	4.5 x 4.0m	14'8" x 13'1"
Kitchen/Dining	5.6 x 4.5m	18'4" x 14'8"
Utility	2.4 x 1.9m	7'9" x 6'2"
Hot Press	1.9 x 1.2m	6'2" x 3'9"
Bathroom	3.7 x 2.3m	12'1" x 7'5"
Bedroom 1	4.3 x 4.2m	14'1" x 13'8"
En suite	1.8 x 2.0m	5'9" x 6'6"
Wardrobe	1.8 x 1.6m	5'9" x 5'2"
Bedroom 2	4.3 x 3.9m	14'1" x 12'8"
Bedroom 3	4.9 x 3.4m	16'1" x 11'2"
FRONTAGE	15.9m	52 ft
AREA	136.2 sq. m.	1466 sq. ft.

HOUSE B-202

A well laid out, charming one and a half storey home. All rooms are immediately accessible off the hallway and landing, which increases the space available. Exterior double doors from the kitchen, such as shown here allow for development and building of a sunroom at a later date if desired.

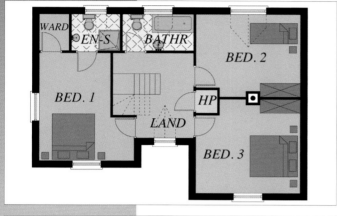

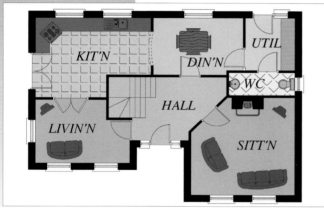

B-202		
Hall	2.8 x 5.0m	9'2" x 16'4"
Sitting Room	4.4 x 4.3m	14'4" x 14'1"
Living Room	2.8 x 4.0m	9'2" x 13'1"
Kitchen	3.5 x 4.9m	11'5" x 16'8"
Dining Room	3.8 x 2.5m	12'5" x 8'2"
Utility	2.3 x 2.1m	7'6" x 6'9"
WC	1.0 x 2.8m	3'3" x 9'2"
Landing	3.7 x 3.4m	12'5" x 11'2"
Bedroom 1	4.7 x 3.0m	15'4" x 9'8"
En suite	2.1 x 1.6m	6'9" x 5'3"
Wardrobe	1.3 x 1.6m	4'3" x 5'3"
Bedroom 2	4.4 x 3.6m	14'4" x 11'8"
Bedroom 3	4.4 x 4.1m	14'4" x 13'5"
Hotpress	1.0 x 0.9m	3'3" x 2'10"
Bathroom	3.0 x 1.6m	9'8" x 5'3"
FRONTAGE	11.6m	38 ft
AREA	147.9 sq. m.	1591 sq. ft.

See page 104 to order this design by Post

HOUSE B-203

An impressive family home. The fact that the front façade is symmetrical helps with the attractiveness of this design. All three bedrooms and indeed the study area, can easily accommodate double beds as desired.

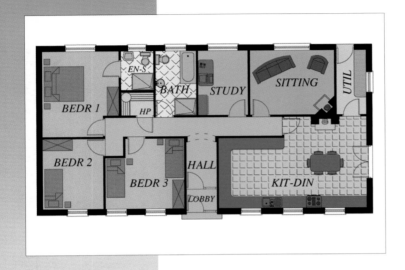

B-203		
Lobby	1.5 x 1.1m	4'9" x 3'6"
Hall	1.5m	4'9"
Kitchen/Dining	7.4 x 4.8m	24'1" x 15'8"
Utility	3.4 x 1.5m	11'2" x 4'9"
Sitting Room	3.7 x 3.4m	12'1" x 11'2"
Study	3.4 x 3.0m	11'2" x 9'8"
Bathroom	3.4 x 2.0m	11'2" x 6'6"
Bedroom 1	4.4 x 3.8m	14'4" x 12'5"
En suite	2.0 x 1.6m	6'6" x 5'3"
Bedroom 2	3.6 x 3.0m	11'8" x 9'8"
Bedroom 3	3.9 x 3.6m	12'8" x 11'8"
Hot press	1.6 x 1.2m	5'3" x 3'9"
FRONTAGE	16.9m	55 ft
AREA	133.3 sq. m.	1435 sq. ft.

See page 101 for plan prices

HOUSE B-204

Something with a difference! The fabulous angled roof is equal in width throughout in order to keep building cost down. The large attic space can easily be converted at a later date if desired.

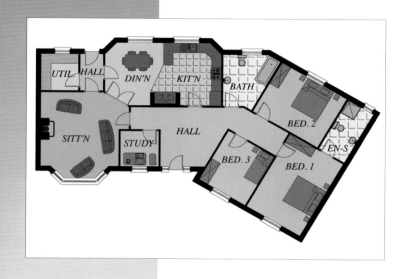

B-204		
Hall	3.7 x 4.1m	12'1" x 13'5"
Study	2.3 x 2.2m	7'6" x 7'2"
Sitting Room	4.7 x 4.6m	15'4" x 15'1"
Dining Room	3.5 x 3.9m	11'5" x 12'8"
Kitchen	3.9 x 3.5m	12'8" x 11'5"
Utility	2.3 x 2.3m	7'5" x 7'6"
Hall	2.3 x 1.4m	7' 6" x 4'6"
Bathroom	3.5 x 3.2m	11'5" x 10'5"
Bedroom 1	5.2 x 3.7m	17'1" x 12'5"
En suite	3.5 x 1.8m	11'5" x 5'9"
Bedroom 2	4.5 x 3.5m	14'8" x 11'5"
Bedroom 3	3.5 x 3.2m	11'5" x 10'5"
FRONTAGE	16.6m	54 ft
AREA	152.3 sq. m.	1638 sq. ft.

HOUSE B-205

This elegant bungalow uses all available space constructively. The circular bay window off the sitting room provides a lot of character. Very often this type of single storey is perfect for a narrow restricted site.

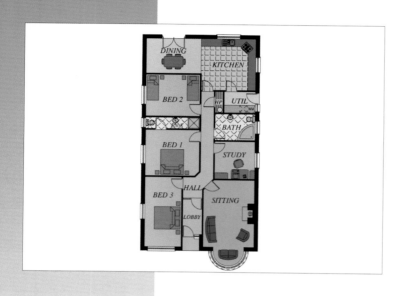

B-205		
Lobby	1.5m	4'9"
Hall	1.0m	3'3"
Sitting Room	5.4 x 3.9m	17'7" x 12'8"
Study	3.1 x 3.0m	10'2" x 9'8"
Bathroom	3.1 x 2.1m	10'2" x 6'9"
Utility	2.4 x 1.7m	7'9" x 5'6"
Hot press	1.7 x 0.6m	5'6" x 1'10"
Kitchen	4.2 x 4.1m	13'8" x 13'5"
Dining Room	2.8 x 4.2m	9'2" x 13'8"
Bedroom 1	4.2 x 3.7m	13'8" x 12'1"
En suite	4.2 x 0.9m	13'8" x 2'9"
Bedroom 2	4.2 x 3.3m	13'8" x 10'8"
Bedroom 3	5.6 x 2.9m	18'4" x 9'5"
FRONTAGE	9.1m	30 ft
AREA	144 sq. m.	1550 sq. ft.

HOUSE B-206

A single storey house with a feature bedroom. This is a very popular type of design. It can be ideal where planning restrictions require a bungalow and a style not quite standard is preferred.

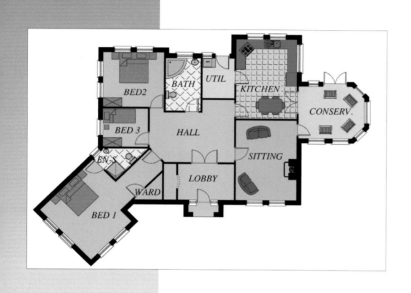

B-206		
Lobby	3.5 x 2.4m	11'5" x 7'9"
Hall	5.3 x 3.2m	17'4" x 10'5"
Sitting Room	5.2 x 3.8m	17'1" x 12'5"
Conservatory	4.2 x 3.4m	13'8" x 11'2"
Kitchen	5.2 x 3.8m	17'1" x 12'5"
Utility	2.6 x 2.0m	8'5" x 6'6"
Bathroom	3.5 x 2.2m	11'5" x 7'2"
Bedroom 1	4.7 x 4.8m	15'4" x 15'8"
En suite	2.0 x 1.7m	6'6" x 5'7"
Bedroom 2	3.8 x 3.6m	12'5" x 11'8"
Bedroom 3	2.8 x 2.5m	9'2" x 8'2"
FRONTAGE	16.9m	55 ft
AREA	152.1 sq. m.	1637 sq. ft.

HOUSE B-207

A superb one storey house. Bay windows are used to very good effect in this design and provide added space to those rooms. The lobby immediately inside the front entrance door is a feature popular with many people

B-207		
Hall	1.3 x 4.2m	4'6" x 13'8"
Living Room	4.6 x 4.2m	15'1" x 13'8"
Kitchen	3.9 x 3.7m	12'8" x 12'1"
Dining	3.9 x 3.5m	12'8" x 11'5"
Utility	3.0 x 2.0m	9'8" x 6'6"
WC	1.3 x 1.8m	4'3" x 5'9"
Hot press	1.3 x 1.1m	4'3" x 3'6"
Bathroom	3.0 x 2.0m	9'8" x 6'6"
Bedroom 1	4.0 x 3.6m	13'1" x 11'8"
En suite	2.8 x 1.0m	9'2" x 3'3"
Bedroom 2	4.1 x 2.4m	13'5" x 7'9"
Bedroom 3	3.4 x 3.0m	11'2" x 9'4"
Bedroom 4	3.4 x 3.1m	11'2" x 10'2"
Hot Press	1.4 x 1.1m	4'5" x 3'7"
FRONTAGE	17.9m	59 ft
AREA	14.9 sq. m.	1452 sq. ft.

See page 104 to order this design by Post

HOUSE B-208

Specifically designed with current planning practice in mind, this superb smaller dwelling is very popular! The indigenous style windows, full gable roof, and bracketed porch combine very well, especially in more sensitive planning areas. The large utility adjacent to the kitchen allows for ample storage space to this area.

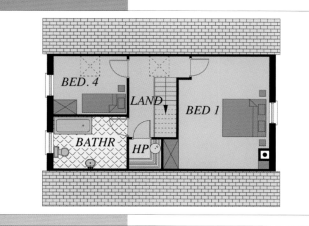

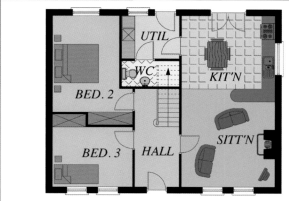

B-208		
Hall	4.6 x 2.0m	15'1" x 6'6"
Sitting Room	4.6 x 4.2m	15'1" x 13'8"
Kitchen	3.4 x 4.2m	11'2" x 13'8"
Utility	2.6 x 2.0m	8'5" x 6'5"
WC	2.6 x 1.2m	8'5" x 3'9"
Landing	2.2 x 3.9m	7'2" x 12'8"
Bedroom 1	5.4 x 4.2m	17'7" x 13'8"
Bedroom 2	4.3 x 3.0m	14'1" x 9'8"
Bedroom 3	2.8 x 3.6m	9'2" x 11'8"
Bedroom 4	3.4 x 2.8m	11'2" x 8'2"
Bathroom	3.4 x 2.5m	11'2" x 8'2"
Hot press	1.3 x 1.4m	4'9" x 4'5"
FRONTAGE	10.6m	35 ft
AREA	134.0 sq. m.	1444 sq. ft.

See page 101 for plan prices

HOUSE B-209

A superb single storey dwelling house. The two pediment roofs on the façade tie in perfectly with the large full hips. The front door is slightly recessed which can protect against the elements more so, especially on an exposed site.

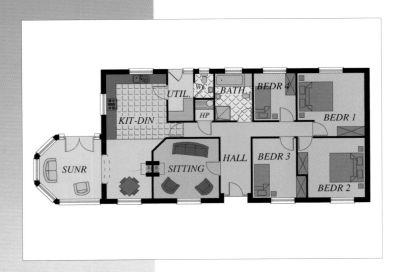

B-209		
Hall	1.8m	5'9"
Sitting Room	3.9 x 3.7m	12'8" x 12'1"
Kitchen	7.7 x 3.1m	25'3" x 10'2"
Sun Room	3.7 x 3.7m	12'1" x 12'1"
Utility	3.2 x 1.5m	10'5" x 4'9"
WC	1.5 x 1.1m	4'9" x 3'6"
Hot press	1.3 x 1.1m	4'3" x 3'6"
Bedroom 1	4.0 x 3.9m	13'1" x 12'9"
Bedroom 2	4.0 x 3.7m	13'1" x 12'1"
Bedroom 3	3.7 x 2.6m	12'1" x 8'5"
Bedroom 4	2.9 x 2.5m	9'5" x 8'2"
Bathroom	2.9 x 2.2m	9'5" x 7'2"
FRONTAGE	20.0m	66 ft
AREA	131.6 sq. m.	1417 sq. ft.

HOUSE *B-210*

A fabulous interior layout married with a superb, well designed exterior. The large dormer window on the first floor landing offers terrific light to this area and the hallway below. All the habitable areas on the ground floor are very easily accessible from each other.

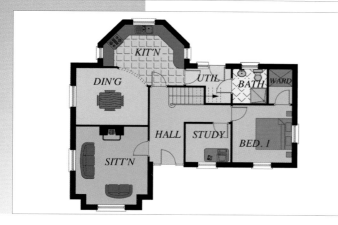

B-210		
Hall	1.9 x 4.3m	6'2" x 14'1"
Sitting Room	4.5 x 4.0m	14'8" x 13'1"
Dining Room	3.3 x 4.0m	10'8" x 13'1"
Kitchen	3.5 x 4.5m	11'5" x 14'8"
Utility	2.0 x 1.4m	6'6" x 4'6"
Study	2.2 x 2.5m	7'2" x 8'2"
Bedroom 1	3.3 x 3.3m	10'8" x 10'8"
Wardrobe	2.0 x 1.3m	6'6" x 4'3"
Bathroom	2.0 x 1.9m	6' 6" x 6'2"
Landing	2.1 x 3.8m	6'9" x 12'5"
Hot press	1.0 x 0.9m	3'3" x 2'10"
Bathroom	2.1 x 2.4m	6'10" x 7' 9"
Bedroom 2	303 x 2.9m	10'8" x 9'5"
En suite	2.0 x 1.9m	6'6" x 6'2"
Wardrobe	2.0 x 0.9	6'6" x 2'10"
Bedroom 3	5.1 x 3.2m	16'7" x 10'5"
Bedroom 4	4.3 x 4.0m	14'1" x 13'1"
Storage	3.8 x 1.0m	12'5" x 3'3"
FRONTAGE	12.6m	41 ft
AREA	156.3 sq. m.	1641 sq. ft

Costs of Building

When working out a budget for your future home always bear in mind ancillary costs such as local authority development charges, conveyancing, landscaping (which can often be a planning condition), supervising engineer and home bond registration. On these pages we indicate the basic cost of the designs in Dream Houseplans brought up to a finished level, to a good quality, standard finish. These prices shown are estimates only and include for strip foundations, fibre cement slates on a cut roof, cavity blockwork external walls, nap plaster finish (which may contradict that shown in our 3-D image), oil fired central heating, sanitaryware supply and fit, plumbing and electrics, first and second fix joinery (red deal throughout), double-glazed white PVC windows, white PVC fascia and soffit, standard septic tank and percolation area and a 1m footpath around the house. The house would be essentially finished to a 'turn key' standard. The following items are excluded from the prices as indicated: painting, tiling, kitchen, fireplace, proprietary effluent treatment system, landscaping, driveway, boundary treatments and any professional or any ancillary fees as mentioned above.

Region 1:

West, north-west and midlands

Region 2:

South, south-east and north-east, up to Louth in the east and Limerick in the west.

Region 3:

Cities, including outlying areas, of Dublin, Cork, Limerick and Galway.

Region 4:

Northern Ireland, add approximately 7-11% for Belfast and Derry and outlying areas.

Many people do not adhere to the prices as estimated above and human nature dictates that people tend to chose more expensive sanitary ware, a more expensive stairs, the more attractive wall finishing etc. Stone and brick are superb, attractive finishes but the cost of the tradesman is generally more expensive than the actual materials in this case and this must be borne in mind. All prices shown are approximate only and are intended as guidelines. They are indicative of a standard tendered contractual situation as of Summer 2005.

House	Region 1 €	Region 2 €	Region 3 €	Region 4 Stg £
A-201	71,800.00	74,700.00	81,300.00	54,900.00
A-202	79,300.00	82,600.00	89,400.00	59,100.00
A-203	79,000.00	82,500.00	89,200.00	59,000.00
A-204	92,500	94,900	101,600.00	72,600
A-205	84,600.00	88,300.00	95,500.00	63,100.00
A-206	94,600.00	98,500.00	106,500.00	70,600.00
A-207	95,800.00	99,900.00	108,000.00	71,600.00
A-208	73,900.00	77,000.00	83,300.00	55,100.00
A-209	92,000.00	95,900.00	103,800.00	68,800.00
B-201	102,600.00	107,100.00	117,400.00	77,900.00
B-202	112,900.00	117,800.00	127,300.00	84,300.00
B-203	101,900.00	106,200.00	114,900.00	76,200.00
B-204	114,800.00	119,600.00	127,300.00	90,100.00
B-205	110,000.00	114,800.00	124,200.00	82,200.00
B-206	117,900.00	122,900.00	131,800.00	88,200.00
B-207	103,100.00	114,100.00	116,200.00	76,000.00
B-208	102,600.00	106,800.00	115,500.00	76,600.00
B-209	100,700.00	104,900.00	113,500.00	75,100.00
B-210	116,500.00	121,600.00	131,400.00	87,000.00
C-201	139,000.00	144,900.00	156,600.00	103,800.00
C-202	119,600.00	124,800.00	134,800.00	89,400.00
C-203	134,600.00	141,400.00	148,900.00	108,400.00
C-204	132,500.00	138,500.00	149,600.00	98,400.00
C-205	137,300.00	143,100.00	154,800.00	102,600.00
C-206	127,300.00	132,700.00	143,500.00	95,100.00
C-207	117,800.00	122,700.00	132,600.00	87,900.00
C-208	149,600.00	155,800.00	167,200.00	112,000.00
C-209	118,900.00	123,900.00	133,900.00	88,900.00
C-210	124,800.00	129,900.00	140,400.00	93,100.00
C-211	119,900.00	125,100.00	135,400.00	89,800.00

House	Region 1 €	Region 2 €	Region 3 €	Region 4 Stg £
C-212	131,700.00	137,200.00	148,400.00	98,300.00
C-213	139,900.00	145,800.00	157,800.00	104,500.00
D-201	157,000.00	163,700.00	176,900.00	117,300.00
D-202	153,200.00	159,700.00	172,600.00	114,400.00
D-203	173,700.00	181,000.00	195,800.00	129,600.00
D-204	152,500.00	159,000.00	171,900.00	113,900.00
D-205	157,900.00	164,700.00	177,900.00	117,900.00
D-206	167,500.00	174,500.00	188,700.00	124,900.00
D-207	169,300.00	176,500.00	190,800.00	126,400.00
D-208	144,300.00	150,400.00	162,600.00	107,700.00
D-209	156,900.00	163,700.00	176,900.00	117,200.00
D-210	151,300.00	157,700.00	170,500.00	112,900.00
D-211	159,000.00	165,700.00	179,300.00	118,800.00
D-212	159,500.00	166,300.00	179,800.00	119,000.00
D-213	177,300.00	184,800.00	199,800.00	134,500.00
D-214	158,900.00	165,500.00	179,900.00	118,700.00
D-215	170,500.00	177,800.00	192,400.00	127,400.00
D-216	167,300.00	172,500.00	186,400.00	123,700.00
D-217	146,600.00	152,700.00	165,100.00	109,400.00
E-201	224,000.00	233,400.00	252,400.00	167,300.00
E-202	187,500.00	195,400.00	211,200.00	139,900.00
E-203	188,900.00	196,900.00	212,700.00	140,800.00
E-204	197,800.00	206,200.00	222,900.00	147,700.00
E-205	201,500.00	210,000.00	226,900.00	150,400.00
E-206	182,600.00	190,200.00	205,900.00	136,300.00
E-207	192,500.00	200,600.00	216,800.00	143,700.00
E-208	184,000.00	191,800.00	207,400.00	137,400.00
E-209	199,600.00	208,000.00	221,800.00	147,000.00
E-210	180,400.00	188,000.00	203,200.00	134,600.00
E-211	200,300.00	208,700.00	225,800.00	149,700.00

Section C

House Designs from 1651 sq. ft. up to 2000 sq. ft.

TIP: Even if your house finish is all-brick or all-stone it is better to have a plaster finished chimney. Stone and brick chimneys frequently cause problems with damp penetration. To counteract this, insist the construction be cavity all the way to the underside of the coping, and apply minimum two coats of a good quality sealant around the chimney above roof level.

HOUSE C-201

An elegant two-storey dwelling. The forward protrusion from the study on left-hand side adds some variety to the front elevation. The large, spacious landing is a central feature of the top floor layout.

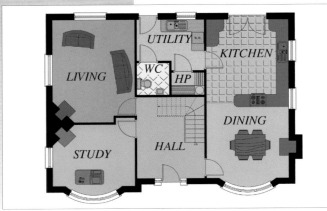

C-201		
Hall	4.0 x 3.2m	13'1" x 10'5"
Kitchen/Dining	7.8 x 3.9m	25'6" x 12'8"
Utility	3.2 x 2.5m	10'5" x 8'2"
WC	1.5 x 1.5m	4'9" x 4'9"
Hot Press	1.6 x 1.1m	5'3" x 3'6"
Study	3.9 x 3.0m	12'8" x 9'8"
Living	5.0 x 3.9m	16'4" x 12'8"
Landing	5.2 x 3.2m	17'2" x 10'6"
Bedroom 1	3.9 x 3.9m	12'8" x 12'8"
En suite	1.8 x 1.8m	5'9" x 5'9"
Wardrobe	2.0 x 1.2m	6'6" x 3'9"
Bedroom 2	4.1 x 2.9m	13'5" x 9'5"
Bedroom 3	4.3 x 3.9m	14'1" x 12'8"
Bedroom 4	3.9 x 3.4m	12'8" x 11'2"
Bathroom	3.0 x 2.5m	9'8" x 8'2"
FRONTAGE	11.8m	39 ft
AREA	181.8 sq. m.	1957 sq. ft

See page 104 to order this design by Post

HOUSE C-202

This attractive single storey house has everything required. The study adjacent to the hallway can obviously double up as a bedroom if required. It is quite possible to finish the front protrusion in alternative finish, such as brick or stone, which gives an imposing, elegant impression.

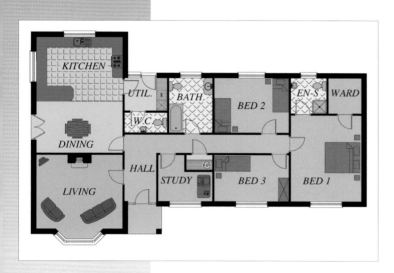

C-202		
Hall	1.8m	5'9"
Study	3.1 x 2.7m	10'2" x 8'9"
Living room	4.9 x 4.4m	16'1" x 14'4"
Kitchen/Dining	6.8 x 4.9m	22'3" x 16'1"
Utility	2.4 x 1.9m	7'9" x 6'2"
WC	2.4 x 1.2m	7'9" x 3'9"
Bedroom 1	5.1 x 4.0m	16'7" x 13'1"
En suite	2.1 x 2.0m	6'9" x 6'5"
Wardrobe	2.1 x 1.9m	6'9" x 6'2"
Bedroom 2	4.2 x 3.2m	13'8" x 10'5"
Bedroom 3	4.2 x 2.7m	13'8" x 8'9"
Bathroom	3.2 x 2.5m	10'5" x 8'2"
Hot Press	1.5 x 0.9m	4'9" x 2'10"
FRONTAGE	19.2m	63 ft
AREA	156.4 sq. m.	1684 sq. ft

Log on to Houseplans.ie to order plans and to quote for changes.

HOUSE C-203

One can see why this style of design is so popular. As with most dwellings, other finishes such as stone or plaster can work equally well from that shown in our image. The spacious walk-in hot press on the first floor is a recommended item.

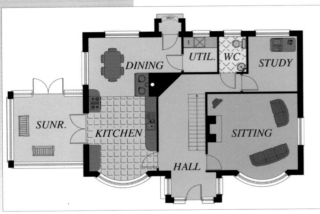

C-203		
Hall	6.8 x 2.5m	22'3" x 8'2"
Sitting Room	4.8 x 4.2m	15'8" x 13'8"
Kitchen/Dining	7.3 x 3.6m	23'10" x 11'8"
Sun Room	3.7 x 3.6m	12'1" x 11'8"
Utility	1.8 x 1.9m	5'9" x 6'2"
WC	1.9 x 1.4m	6'2" x 4'6"
Study	3.0 x 2.6m	9'8" x 8'5"
Landing	3.4 x 2.0m	11'2" x 6'6"
Hot Press	2.3 x 1.5m	7'6" x 4'9"
Bedroom 1	4.4 x 3.6m	14'4" x 11'8"
En suite	2.5 x 2.4m	8'2" x 7'9"
Bedroom 2	3.8 x 2.8m	12'5" x 9'2"
Bedroom 3	4.8 x 4.0m	15'8" x 13'1"
Bedroom 4	4.4 x 3.2m	14'4" x 10'5"
Bathroom	2.6 x 1.8m	8'5" x 5'9"
FRONTAGE	15.7m	51 ft
AREA	184.8 sq. m.	1990 sq. ft

See page 101 for plan prices

HOUSE C-204

A simple but tasteful design. Such a dwelling as this can be relatively inexpensive to build. The master bedroom and bathroom upstairs especially are very large in size.

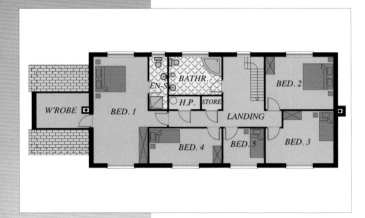

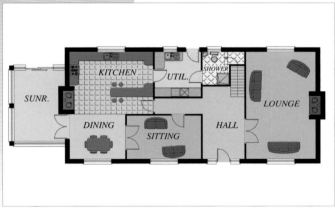

C-204		
Hall	5.9 x 5.0m	19'4" x 16'4"
Lounge	4.6 c 7.3m	15'1" x 23'10"
Sitting Room	4.9 x 3.0m	16'1" x 9'8"
Kitchen/Dining	7.3 x 5.5m	23'10" x 18'0"
Sun Room	4.9 x 3.4m	16'1" x 11'2"
Utility	3.0 x 3.0m	9'8" x 9'8"
Shower Room	2.7 x 1.7m	9'0" x 5'9"
Landing	4.9 x 7.6m	16'1" x 24'9"
Store	1.4 x 0.9m	4'6" x 2'10"
Hot Press	2.1 x 0.9m	6'10" x 2'10"
Bedroom 1	3.7 x 7.4m	12'1" x 24'3"
En suite	1.2 x 3.7m	3'9" x 12'1"
Wardrobe	3.6 x 2.4m	11'8" x 7'9"
Bedroom 2	4.6 x 3.7m	15'1" x 12'1"
Bedroom 3	3.7 x 4.6m	12'1" x 15'1"
Bedroom 4	4.9 x 2.4m	16'1" x 7'9"
Bedroom 5	2.7 x 2.4m	8'9" x 7'9"
Bathroom	3.6 x 2.7m	11'8" x 8'9"
FRONTAGE	16.7m	55 ft
AREA	176.0 sq. m.	1894 sq. ft

HOUSE C-205

This superb residence has a charming frontage. This design can suit just about any type of finish, whether it be plaster, brick or stone. An attached garage is often more practical than a detached one owing to our climate.

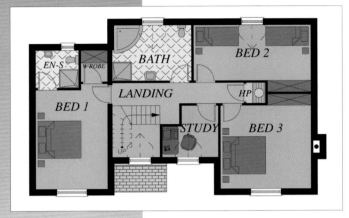

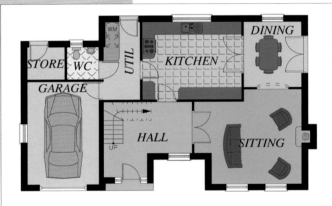

C-205		
Hall	4.1 x 3.6m	13'5" x 11'8"
Sitting Room	5.0 x 4.6m	16'42 x 15'1"
Dining Room	3.1 x 2.7m	10'2" x 8'9"
Kitchen	4.6 x 5.7m	15'1" x 12'1"
Utility	3.7 x 1.7m	12'1 x 5'6"
WC	1.6 x 1.5m	5'3" x 4'9"
Store	1.7 x 1.5m	5'6" x 4'9"
Garage	5.0 x 3.3m	16'4" x 10'8"
Landing	1.0m	3'3"
Bedroom 1	4.8 x 3.4m	15'8" x 11'2"
En suite	2.0 x 1.8m	6'6" x 5'9"
Wardrobe	1.3 x 1.5m	4'3" x 4'9"
Bedroom 2	5.5 x 2.6m	18'5" x 8'5"
Bedroom 3	4.6 x 4.2m	15'1" x 13'8"
Bathroom	3.7 x2.6m	12'1" x 8'5"
Study	2.4 x 2.6m	7'9" x 8'5"
FRONTAGE	13.4m	44 ft
AREA	179.6 sq. m.	1933 sq. ft

**Phone
00 353 56
7771300 to order
plans by credit card
from outside the
Republic of Ireland**

HOUSE C-206

A surprisingly simple but very elegant dwelling. Sunrooms such as this one are often built at a later date from the main house, but it is hugely advantageous to put in the foundations with the main construction. The kitchen, dining room, sun room and sitting room areas work as one common space.

C-206		
Hall	5.2 x 2.1m	17'1" x 6'9"
Sitting Room	5.0 x 4.0	16'4" x 13'1"
Study	3.5 x 3.2m	11'5" x 10'5"
Kitchen/Dining	7.8 x 3.8m	25'6" x 12'5"
Sun Room	2.9 x 2.7m	9'5" x 8'9"
Utility	1.8 x 1.6m	5'9" x 5'3"
WC	1.3 X 1.6m	4'3" x 5'3"
Hot Press	1.6 x 0.9m	5'3" x 2'10"
Landing	0.9m	2'10"
Bedroom 1	4.6 x 3.8m	15'1" x 12'5"
En suite	1.6 x 1.6m	5'3" x 5'3"
Wardrobe	1.6 x 1.3m	5'3" x 4'3"
Bedroom 2	4.4 x 3.5m	14'4" x 11'5"
Bedroom 3	3.9 x 3.2m	12'8" x 10'5"
Bedroom 4	3.3 x 3.7m	10'8" x 12'1"
Bathroom	2.3 x 2.4m	7'6" x 7'9"
FRONTAGE	10.1m	33 ft
AREA	166.6 sq. m.	1793 sq. ft

See page 104 to order this design by Post

HOUSE C-207

This charming bungalow is surprisingly spacious. All four bedrooms are quite large. The raised parapets to the roof confirm the building to be indigenous in style and therefore pleasing to the planning authorities.

C-207		
Hall	2.2m	7'2"
Kitchen	6.1 x 4.0m	20' 0" x 13'1"
Dining	3.5 x 3.2m	11'5" x 10'5"
Sitting Room	4.8 x 4.2m	15'8" x 13'8"
Utility	1.7 x 1.7m	5'6" x 5'6"
WC	1.9 x 1.4m	6'2" x 4'6"
Bathroom	3.5 x 2.3m	11'5" x 7'6"
Bedroom 1	4.6 x 3.7m	15'12 x 12'1"
En suite	2.2 x 1.2m	7'2" x 3'9"
Bedroom 2	4.1 x 3.4m	13'5" x 11'2"
Bedroom 3	3.5 x 2.6m	11'5" x 8'5"
Bedroom 4	4.6 x 3.9m	15'1" x 12'8"
FRONTAGE	17.4m	57 ft
AREA	154.0 sq. m.	1658 sq. ft

HOUSE C-208

A spacious, American style family residence. The key rooms downstairs are very much open plan in this fabulous layout. The intricate rooflines combine to create a very elegant exterior.

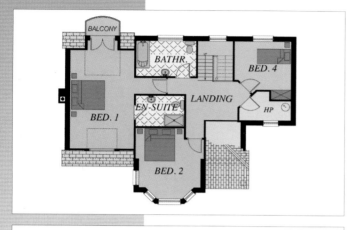

C-208		
Porch	2.4 x 1.3m	7'9" x 4'3"
Hall	5.3 x 4.5m	17'4" x 14'8"
Kitchen/Dining	6.3 x 4.0m	20'7" x 13'1"
Sitting Room	7.3 x 3.9m	23'10" x 12'8"
Utility	3.5 x 1.7m	11'5" x 4'3"
WC	1.5 x 1.3m	4'9" x 4'3"
Landing	3.1 x 2.4m	10'1" x 7'9"
Hot Press	3.1 x 1.2m	10'2" x 3'9"
Bedroom 1	6.1 x 3.8m	20'0" x 12'5"
En suite	2.9 x 1.9m	9'5" x 6'2"
Bedroom 2	3.7 x 3.7m	12'1" x 12'1"
Bedroom 3	4.9 x 3.1m	16'1" x 10'2"
Bedroom 4	3.1 x 3.0m	10'2" x 9'8"
Bathroom	3.6 x 2.2m	11'8" x 7'2"
FRONTAGE	13.9m	46 ft
AREA	184.8 sq. m.	1990 sq. ft

See page 101 for plan prices

HOUSE C-209

Full hips on a single storey such as shown in this image add immense character. There is a surprising amount of space in the five bedrooms. The large central bathroom acts as a main feature.

C-209		
Hall	1.8m	5'9"
Living Room	4.5 x 4.0m	14'8" x 13'1"
Kitchen	5.6 x 4.8m	18'4" x 15'8"
Utility	2.0 x 1.7m	6'6" x 5'6"
Hot Press	1.7 x 1.5m	5'6" x 4'9"
Bedroom 1	4.3 x 3.6m	14'1" x 11'8"
En suite	1.8 x 1.5m	5'9" x 4'9"
Bedroom 2	4.9 x 3.3m	16'1" x 10'8"
En suite	1.8 x 1.5m	5'9" x 4'9"
Bedroom 3	4.0 x 3.0m	13'1" x 9'8"
Bedroom 4	3.6 x 2.9m	11'8" x 9'5"
Bedroom 5	4.0 x 2.5m	13'1" x 8'2"
Bathroom	3.6 x 2.3m	11'8" x 7'6"
FRONTAGE	17.8m	58 ft
AREA	155.5 sq. m.	1674 sq. ft

HOUSE C-210

An attractive multi-room dwelling house. The use of angles is very effective in the central hall area. The double flue chimney as shown here allows for a stove or aga in the kitchen area as desired.

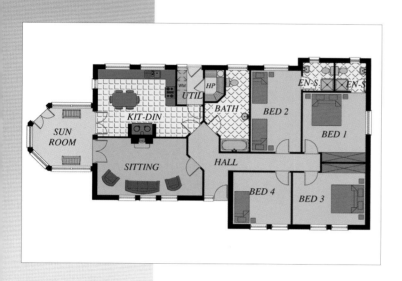

C-210		
Hall	1.7m	5'6"
Sitting Room	6.4 x 3.6m	21'0" x 11'8"
Sun Room	3.7 x 3.7m	12'1" x 12'1"
Kitchen/Dining	6.5 x 4.3m	21'3" x 14'1"
Utility	2.4 x 1.6m	7'9" x 5'3"
Hot Press	1.2 x 2.0m	3'9" x 6'6"
Bathroom	5.2 x 2.7m	17'0" x 8'9"
Bedroom 1	4.4 x 3.9m	14'4" x 12'8"
En suite	1.9 x 1.8m	6'2" x 5'9"
Bedroom 2	5.2 x 3.1m	17'1" x 10'2"
En suite	1.9 x 1.8m	6'2" x 5'9"
Bedroom 3	4.4 x 4.0m	14'4" x 13'1"
Bedroom 4	3.6 x 3.3m	11'8" x 10'8"
FRONTAGE	17.1m	56 ft
AREA	163.0 sq. m.	1755 sq. ft

HOUSE C-211

A practical yet beautiful mid-sized dwelling. As can be seen all upper floor space is used to full effect. A sunroom such as this off the living room may be omitted for construction at a later date.

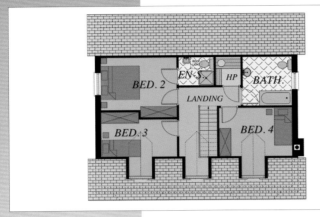

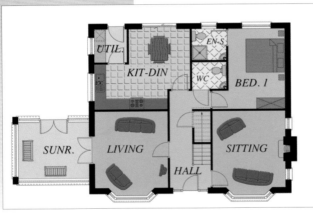

C-211		
Hall	5.2 x 1.2m	17'0" x 3'9"
Sitting Room	4.2 x 3.8m	13'8" x 12'5"
Living Room	4.2 x 3.8m	13'8" x 12'5"
Sun Room	3.7 x 3.1m	12'1" x 10'2"
Kitchen	5.0 x 4.3m	16'4" x 14'1"
Utility	1.8 x 1.7m	5'9" x 5'6"
WC	1.8 x 1.4m	5'9" x 4'6"
Bedroom 1	4.3 x 3.0m	14'1" x 9'8"
En suite	1.8 x 1.7m	5'9" x 5'6"
Bedroom 2	3.9 x 2.8m	12'8" x 9'2"
En suite	1.8 x 1.5m	5'9" x 4'9"
Bedroom 3	3.9 x 2.4m	12'8" x 7'9"
Bedroom 4	3.8 x 2.6m	12'5" x 8'5"
Bathroom	2.6 x 2.5m	8'5" x 8'2"
Landing	1.0m	3'3"
Hot Press	1.5 x 1.3m	4'9" x 4'3"
FRONTAGE	14.6m	48 ft
AREA	157.0 sq. m.	1690 sq. ft

HOUSE C-212

A superb attractive family home. The central kitchen area is easily accessible off all room to the ground floor. The symmetrical style on the exterior combines very well with the hipped roof.

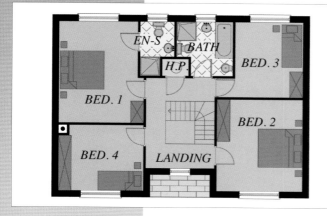

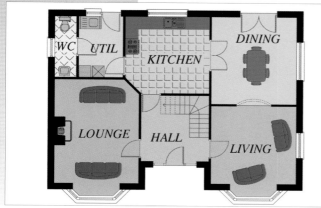

C-212		
Hall	3.1 x 3.1m	10'2" x 10'2"
Living Room	3.9 x 3.7m	12'8" x 12'1"
Dining Room	4.1 x 3.9m	13'5" x 12'8"
Kitchen	3.8 x 3.7m	12'5" x 12'1"
Utility	2.9 x 2.0m	9'5" x 6'6"
WC	2.9 x 1.0m	9'5" x 3'3"
Lounge	4.9 x 3.9m	16'1" x 12'8"
Landing	1.1m	3'6"
Bedroom 1	4.8 x 3.6m	15'8" x 11'8"
En suite	2.5 x 1.5m	8'2" x 4'9"
Bedroom 2	4.3 x 3.9m	14'1" x 12'8"
Bedroom 3	3.5 x 3.1m	11'5" x 10'2"
Bedroom 4	3.9 x 3.1m	12'8" x 11'8"
Bathroom	2.6 x 2.5m	8'5" x 8'2"
Hot Press	1.2 x 0.8m	3'9" x 2'6"
FRONTAGE	11.7m	38 ft
AREA	172.2 sq. m.	1854 sq. ft

45

HOUSE C-213

This family home blends practicality and space internally with simplicity and elegance on the exterior. A large WC to the ground floor is a necessity under the current building regulations. The windows as shown are vertically emphasised in keeping with what is considered good planning and building practice nowadays.

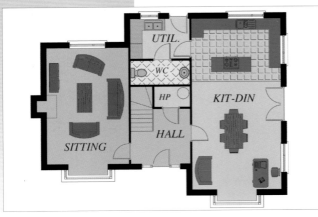

C-213		
Hall	3.0 x 2.8m	9'8" x 9'2"
Kitchen/Dining	9.0 x 4.5m	29'5" x 14'8"
Utility	3.0 x 2.1m	9'8" x 6'9"
WC	3.0 x 1.3m	9'8" x 4'3"
Sitting Room	6.1 x 4.1m	20'0" x 16'5"
Hot Press	1.8 x 1.0m	5'9" x 3'3"
Landing	3.0 x 5.1m	9'8" x 16'7"
Bedroom 1	4.5 x 3.4m	14'8" x 11'2"
En suite	2.5m 1.5m	8'2" x 4'9"
Wardrobe	1.9 x 1.5m	6'2" x 4'9"
Bedroom 2	4.5 x 3.9m	14'8" x 12'8"
Bedroom 3	4.1 x 3.0m	13'5" x 9'8"
Bedroom 4	4.1 x 3.0m	13'5" x 9'8"
Bathroom	3.0 x 2.4m	9'8" x 7'9"
FRONTAGE	12.5m	41 ft
AREA	183.0 sq. m.	1970 sq. ft

Garden Design

Gardens have been a treasured part of human culture from ancient times to the present day. Over time, gardens have had many functional uses – areas for relaxation, food production, and plant collections.

Tastes in gardening styles vary as much as in other aspects of living. What appeals to one person may not appeal to another. The test of a good garden design is whether it appeals to you. This articles sets out to help you create a garden that is visually pleasing and functional for you.

The creation of a garden involves design, planning and construction. Ongoing maintenance is essential to realise the potential of your planned garden.

Design and Planning

The ideal time to start designing and planning your garden is when you start designing your house. Your home environment consists of your house and your garden, neither should be seen in isolation from the other. Equally your house and garden are part of their surrounding landscape. What is appropriate in an urban setting may not be suitable in a rural landscape and vice versa.

There are distinct advantages in consulting a landscape designer at the stage when you are designing your house. The assistance of a professional will help you to make best use of the features of your site, e.g. retaining existing trees. Having a design for your garden from an early stage may save you construction costs. Your builder, as part of the general earthworks, may carry out the shaping of the land for your garden. Additionally, the most cost-effective time for the installation of services, i.e. water and electricity, is at the house-building stage. Thought should be given to the position of service manholes to avoid them being put in a conspicuous place, as they can be unsightly.

Remember there is no need to do everything at once. The design you prepare at this early stage may be implemented over a period of time.

When designing your house you will have thought of the people who will be living in it. The same principle applies when designing your garden. When designing a garden, you will need a wish list of features to incorporate. The people who will use the garden will obviously influence the list. If you are re-designing an existing garden it is also important to decide whether there are features that you would like to retain. It is unlikely that everything on your wish list will be completely fulfilled, however setting down those things that are a priority to you should ensure that the most important features are incorporated. Examples of things for your wish list may include: a paved area/patio, wildlife area, vegetable plot, play area, utility area (bins, composters, clothes line), trees, plants, lawn. Try to include as many items on the wish list as possible in your garden but don't cram in so many that the overall appearance is sacrificed.

The next step in preparing a design is to assess your site. Find the north point; consider which areas of the garden will get the most sun. Consider areas in the garden that will be sheltered or exposed. Make a note of the views to be retained and those that need screening. Remember views from inside the house will be important. Look at the topography/lie of the land and consider how this will influence the positioning of items on your wish list. Take note of existing features, especially planting, trees or a stream.

Assess your soil. Check the depth of topsoil that is above the sub-soil. This is obvious by a change in colour and texture. A good topsoil depth is 300mm. Consider the structure of your soil - is the soil heavy or sandy? The structure of sandy, light soils can be improved by incorporating composts and well-rotted manures to add humus and nutrients. Heavy soils may require drainage or additional treatments to improve their structure for planting. Test the soil pH level. If it is below 7, the soil is acid; if it is 7, the soil is neutral; if it is above 7, the soil is alkaline. The pH will influence the range of plants that may be grown in your garden.

As your garden and house are part of a single entity, the style of both should be consistent and in harmony with each other. Access to the garden from the house is very important. Direct access from main living areas to the garden creates an easy transition from indoors to out. This allows you to use your garden more frequently.

The look and feel of your garden should be as personal to you as the style of your house. It is crucial to decide on the garden's overall look before embarking on its detailed design. If you like everything orderly and neat, a formal garden may be for you. If you prefer more casual styles that look more like a simple setting for plants, an informal design would be more likely to satisfy. Informal gardens are usually more adaptable to family use, with the lawn providing opportunities for play.

Other influences on your choice of design style could include environmental considerations, colour, plants you like, gardens you have visited, inspiration from magazines or photographs and your budget. The time required to maintain your preferred design, together with the skill/knowledge level required, need to be borne in mind.

The final stage of preparing your design is to prepare a drawing of the plan of your proposed garden. You may do this yourself or alternatively have a professional do it for you. It is advisable to have a detailed plan, including construction specifications, if you opt to have a landscape contractor carry out the construction of your garden. Working to clear instructions will save time and money. If you are unclear about the final design of your garden, costly mistakes can be made during construction, e.g. incorrect positioning of patios where they do not receive optimum sunlight.

Construction

Your first decision in relation to construction is who is going to build your garden, i.e. whether you will do it yourself or engage outside contractors. Decide whether you are going to carry out the work in a series of phases or in one go. The season of the year, the climate, the time you have available to spend on the project and your finances are some of the factors that will influence this decision.

There are various stages in the construction of a garden.

• Clearing the site
Your first job may be to clear your site, i.e. remove all debris, builder's rubble. In recent years, the disposal of

builder's waste has become increasingly difficult and expensive. Consider whether any of the material would be suitable for use as filling/foundations for hard landscape areas. Anyone disposing of waste must follow the guidelines and conditions set out by their Local Authority, permits are required where previously these were not necessary. Unwanted, unsafe, or overgrown, vegetation/trees, including roots, should be removed to leave a clean site. Mechanically or chemically remove weeds. If using herbicides be sure to follow the manufacturer's instructions carefully and wear appropriate protective clothing.

• Earthworks

Ground compaction is common after building works. To remedy, the soil should be broken up using a digger or other mechanical device. Land drainage should be installed at this stage if necessary. It may be helpful to employ specialist advice for this purpose.

Once compaction and drainage have been dealt with, the next step is to shape your site to suit the design. Some areas may need to be excavated to allow foundations and sub-bases to be constructed for hard landscape areas, e.g. avenues, patios and paths. The soil may need to be graded/sloped. Major gradient changes should be made in the sub-soil layer, with the top-soil spread back to a minimum depth of 300mm to make the final land shape.

While earth shaping is being carried out, services should be installed throughout the site in the required positions, i.e. electricity cables and water pipes for taps, water features or irrigation systems. It is always helpful to install ducting so that you can adapt to future needs. The ducts need to be laid at the correct depth and marked so that they will be recognised during any possible future excavations.

Soil amelioration works, i.e. addition of organic matter to light sandy soils, or addition of sands to heavy soils should be carried out now. It is very beneficial to incorporate well-rotted farmyard manure, spent mushroom compost or another organic compost to any areas that are to be planted.

• Boundaries

Boundaries have many functions including delineating your property, protecting your garden from animals and trespass, providing shelter and privacy. The boundaries of individual sites are usually marked using living materials, such as hedgerows, hedges or trees, fencing, walls, or a combination of these.

There is an endless range of species that can be used in the creation of living material boundaries. In the countryside, an indigenous mixed species hedgerow will blend with the surrounding landscape. Species to include might be hawthorn, blackthorn, holly, hazel, gorse and fuchsia. Griselinia, Olearia and Escallonia species are tolerant of the growing conditions in coastal areas. In a formal setting Buxus (Box) and Yew may be suitable choices. In rural settings broadleaved deciduous trees are the most appropriate species to use, e.g. oak, sycamore, beech, chestnut or ash. Good ground preparation is crucial to the success of all planting. Planting should always be well protected until it has become established. Formative pruning will need to be carried out on hedging from an early age.

There is a wide range of fencing materials available, e.g. smooth planed timber, rustic timber, iron, steel, plastic, concrete and bamboo. Ensure that uprights are adequately supported. There is a wide choice of wall materials including blocks, brick, stone and unit blocks (e.g. madoc block). Walls may be rendered/finished in a number of ways, e.g. pebble dash, nap plaster, pigmented plasters and paint. Walls require appropriate concrete foundations. Your Local Authority may have regulations about the construction of boundary walls so check these out before proceeding.

• Ground plane materials

The ground plane of your garden could be thought of as the floor of your garden. Similar to your house floors, you need to select different coverings. These coverings might include lawns, wildflower meadows, patios, decking, gravel areas, concrete or tarmacadam. The construction of each covering has its own requirements.

For lawns or wildflower meadows, the soil needs to be

cultivated to a fine till before seeding or turfing. Lawns or meadows are usually sown or turfed between the months of April and September when there is generally more suitable weather and ground working conditions.

There is an every increasing range of hard landscape materials available. These are used for patios, paths and so on. Unit pavers such as bricks, setts, concrete slabs and natural stone are amongst the choices of materials that can be used.

Timber decking is a popular alternative to the traditional patio at present. While they require some maintenance, decking materials can be very versatile and useful on difficult sites. In coastal areas, decking is in keeping with the maritime surroundings.

Changes in ground gradients are accommodated by steps and ramps. Ensure steps are designed with an appropriate rise; 150mm is regarded as suitable in an outdoor environment. Non-smooth construction materials are best for the threads of the steps to avoid them being hazardous, especially when wet. Ramps are desirable to allow easy access for people with reduced mobility, e.g. elderly people, wheelchair users or children in buggies. Ramps are also an advantage to facilitate wheelbarrows and wheelie bins.

• Planting

Plants are the key element in your garden to ensure that it looks attractive and becomes a place where you will want to spend time. There are a number of plant categories, including trees, shrubs, herbaceous material, bulbs, ground cover, climbers, annuals and ornamental grasses. Plants are living organisms so they have requirements for life, including adequate light and water, nutrition and maintenance. As stated earlier, good ground preparation is essential to the success of plants in your garden.

When choosing plants, consider their ultimate size and shape, their colour, their scent, the type of soil and growing conditions they need and their function in the design of your garden.

The combination of individual plants to produce an aesthetically pleasing planting scheme requires knowledge and experience. Helpful advice can be obtained from good garden centres, gardening magazines and landscape consultants.

• Water

The inclusion of man-made water features in your design, though sometimes challenging to construct, are very rewarding. If you have a water feature in your garden, you need to consider the source of water to be used, ways of containing the water, and re-circulating the flow if the feature involves moving water. There are various pumps available and you should seek professional advice on the appropriate equipment for the water feature you desire.

• Other elements

Gazebos, pergolas, seating, containers and sculptures are additional elements that may be part of your design. You may decide to buy ready-made items or alternatively to have them assembled/constructed on site.

• Maintenance

All gardens require some degree of maintenance to realise the full potential of their design. Maintenance should be given consideration at the design stage. The amount of time needed to maintain the garden and the level of knowledge required to do so will have influenced your final design. Some designs are low maintenance, e.g. gravel gardens. Others are high maintenance, e.g. rose gardens.

Maintenance is generally divided into hard landscape maintenance and soft landscape maintenance. Hard landscape maintenance work includes cleaning paved areas, treating timbers, iron and other corrodible materials, and cleaning water features. This is usually seasonal work that can be carried out annually.

Soft landscape maintenance work is much more time consuming. Soft landscape maintenance includes lawn maintenance, pruning, hedge cutting, weed and pest control, watering, applying manures/fertilizers and planting. While some of these tasks are seasonal, many need to be carried on a regular basis for most of the year.

Gardens are dynamic and evolve over time. They provide us with an opportunity to work with and against the elements and allow us to appreciate the power of nature.

Article compiled by AnnMarie Mahon (BAgrSc – Landscape Horticulture) of Mahon Landscape Designs, Blackwell, Bennettsbridge, Co Kilkenny, tel: 056-7727848, mobile: 086-8861906.

Section D

House Designs from 2001 sq. ft. up to 2500 sq. ft.

TIP: A typical payment structure between you and your builder can be as follows: substructure (ground floor) 25%, wallplate level 25%, roof completion 25%, second fixing 12.5 % and final completion (after snagging) 12.5%.

HOUSE D-201

This style of house has proved very popular both with homeowners and builders alike down through the years. The arched window to the landing area helps balance the frontage. The large toilet adjacent to the utility room is a necessity in keeping with current building regulations.

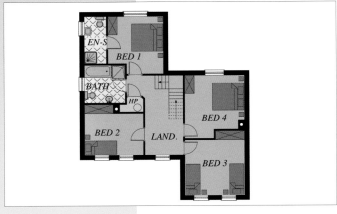

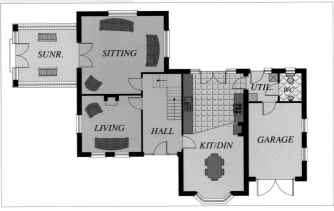

D-201		
Hall	5.2 x 2.4m	17'1" x 7'9"
Living Room	3.8 x 3.7m	12'5" x 12'1"
Sitting Room	5.2 x 5.2m	17'1" x 17'1"
Sun Room	3.6 x 3.4m	11'8" x 11'2"
Kitchen/Dining	7.9 x 3.8m	25'0" x 12'5"
Utility	1.9 x 1.8m	6'2" x 5'9"
WC	1.9 x 1.4m	6'2" x 4'6"
Landing	5.2 x 2.4m	17'1" x 7'9"
Hot Press	1.5 x 1.0m	4'9" x 3'3"
Bedroom 1	3.8 x 3.5m	12'5" x 11'5"
En suite	3.1 x 1.4m	10'2" x 4'6"
Bedroom 2	3.7 x 3.3m	12'1" X 10'8"
Bedroom 3	4.2 x 3.8m	13'8" x 12'5"
Bedroom 4	3.8 x 3.6m	12'5" x 11'8"
Bathroom	2.6 x 1.7m	8'5" x 5'6"
Garage	3.9 x 3.4m	12'8" x 11'2"
FRONTAGE	14.4m	47 ft
AREA	205.5 sq. m.	2212 sq. ft.

See page 104 to order this design by Post

HOUSE D-202

This enticing dormer bungalow has no less than five spacious bedrooms. The 45° pitch as shown here allows for around 90% of the first floor area to be utilised efficiently. The kitchen area is conveniently open to the adjacent dining area, which leads to the outside through french doors as shown

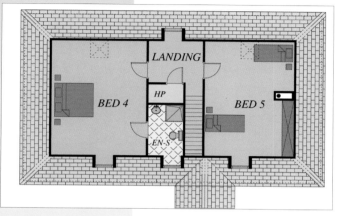

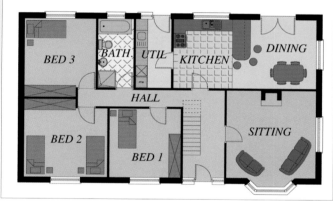

D-202		
Hall	4.6 x 2.1m	15'1" x 6'9"
Sitting Room	4.6 x 4.5m	15'1" x 14'8"
Kitchen/Dining	7.2 x 3.6m	23'6" x 11'8"
Utility	3.6 x 1.8m	11'8" x 5'9"
Bedroom 1	3.6 x 3.6m	11'8" x 11'8"
Bedroom 2	4.2 x 4.1m	13'8" x 13'5"
Bedroom 3	4.1 x 3.6m	13'5" x 11'8"
Bathroom	3.6 x 1.8m	11'8" x 5'9"
Landing	2.8 x 2.2m	9'2" x 7'2"
Hot Press	1.8 x 1.0m	5'9" x 3'3"
Bedroom 4	6.1 x 4.9m	20'0" x 16'1"
En suite	2.7 x 1.8m	8'9" x 5'9"
Bedroom 5	6.1 x 4.6m	20'0" x 15'1"
FRONTAGE	15.3m	50 ft
AREA	200.4 sq. m.	2157 sq. ft.

See page 101 for plan prices

HOUSE D-203

There is a good 'flow' between the main habitable rooms in this house. Ample use of double doors allows for travel right around the ground floor without crossing the main hallway. This type of overhang bay window is an attractive alternative to the standard type of bay roof.

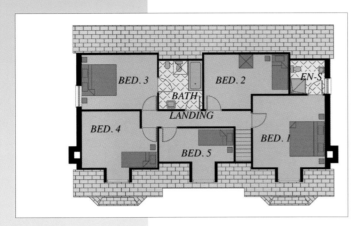

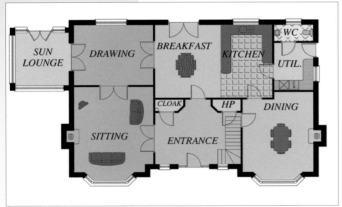

D-203		
Entrance	4.1 x 3.1m	13'5" x 10'2"
Cloak	1.5 x 0.7m	4'9" x 2'3"
Hot Press	1.5 x 0.7m	4'9" x 2'3"
Dining Room	4.9 x 4.1m	16'1" x 13'5"
Kitchen/Breakfast	6.9 x 4.4m	22'6" x 14'4"
Utility	2.9 x 2.3m	9'5" x 7'5"
WC	2.3 x 1.0m	7'5" x 3'3"
Drawing Room	4.7 x 3.6m	15'4" x 11'8"
Sun Lounge	3.2 x 3.1m	10'5" x 10'2"
Sitting Room	5.2 x 4.7m	17'1" x 15'3"
Landing	0.9m	2'10"
Bedroom 1	4.1 x 4.1m	13'5" x 13'5"
En suite	1.9 x 2.0m	6'2" x 6'6"
Bedroom 2	4.8 x 3.3m	15'8" x 10'8"
Bedroom 3	4.4 x 3.1m	14'4" x 10'2"
Bedroom 4	4.4 x 3.2m	14'4" x 10'5"
Bedroom 5	4.3 x 1.9m	14'1" x 6'2"
Bathroom	2.5 x 2.8m	8'2" x 9'2"
FRONTAGE	14.6m	48 ft
AREA	227.1 sq. m.	2445 sq. ft.

HOUSE D-204

A distinctive asymmetrical two storey. Use of stone such as shown here can be very cost effective while still giving this classical appearance. The living room can sometimes be used as an extra bedroom, if necessary.

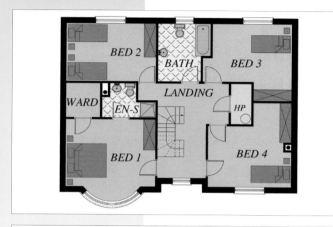

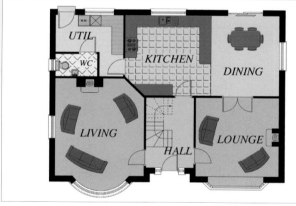

D-204		
Hall	3.8 x 2.4m	12'5" x 7'9"
Lounge	4.3 x 4.2m	14'1" X 13'8"
Kitchen/Dining	7.9 x 4.3m	25'9" x 14'1"
Utility	3.5 x 1.9m	11'5" x 6'2"
WC	2.1 x 1.2m	6'9" x 3'9"
Living Room	5.2 x 4.6m	17'1" x 15'1"
Landing	5.0 x 2.4m	16'4" x 7'9"
Hot Press	2.1 x 1.0m	6'9" x 3'3"
Bedroom 1	4.6 x 3.5m	15'1'" x 11'5"
En suite	1.8 x 1.7m	5'9" x 5'6"
Wardrobe	1.8 x 1.7m	5'9" x 5'6"
Bedroom 2	4.5 x 3.0m	14'8" x 9'8"
Bedroom 3	4.0 x 3.0m	13'1" x 9'8"
Bedroom 4	4.2 x 3.2m	13'8" x 10'5"
FRONTAGE	12.1m	40 ft
AREA	19.6 sq. m.	2148 sq. ft.

**Phone
00 353 56
7771300 to order
plans by credit card
from outside the
Republic of Ireland**

HOUSE D-205

An imposing, superb single storey dwelling. This American style design has become increasingly popular over the years. The large, spacious bedrooms on the left are kept strictly separate from the habitable areas on the right-hand side.

D-205		
Hall	4.3m	14'1"
WC	2.6 x 1.3m	8'5" x 4'3"
Sitting Room	6.2 x 5.4m	20'3" x 17'7"
Kitchen/Dining	7.5 x 4.9m	24'6" x 16'1"
Utility	3.4 x 2.9m	11'2" x 9'5"
Sun Room	6.2 x 4.8m	20'3" x 15'8"
Hot Press	2.4 x 1.3m	7'8" x 4'3"
Bedroom 1	6.1 x 4.8m	20'0" x 15'8"
Wardrobe	2.8 x 1.8m	9'2" x 5'9"
En suite	3.6 x 2.0m	11'8" x 6'6"
Bedroom 2	5.1 x 4.8m	16'7" x 15'8"
En suite	2.9 x 2.0m	9'5" x 6'6"
Bathroom	3.1 x 2.9m	10'2" x 9'5"
FRONTAGE	19.5m	62 ft
AREA	206.5 sq. m.	2223 sq. ft.

HOUSE D-206

An attractive dormer dwelling with a distinctive roof. The kitchen dining area in particular is fabulously spacious. Both family room and lounge have bay windows, but they are both unique in style and height.

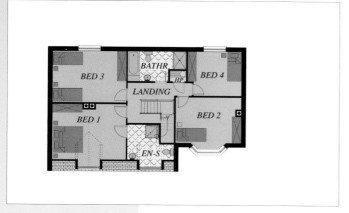

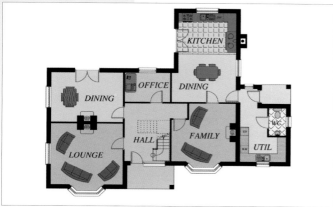

D-206

Hall	4.2 x 3.2m	13'8" x 10'5"
Lounge	4.4 x 5.0m	14'4" x 16'4"
Dining Room	3.6 x 5.0m	11'82" x 16'4"
Office	2.1 x 3.1m	6'8" x 10'5"
Kitchen Dining	6.4 x 4.0m	21'0" x 13'1"
Utility	3.9 x 3.2m	12'8" x 10'5"
WC	2.0 x 1.2m	6'6" x 3'9"
Family Room	4.5 x 4.2m	14'8" x 13'8"
Landing	2.8 x 3.2m	9'2" x 10'5"
Bedroom 1	5.0 x 3.9m	16'4" x 12'8"
En suite	2.5 x 2.2m	8'2" x 7'2"
Bedroom 2	4.5 x 3.2m	14'8" x 10'5"
Bedroom 3	5.0 x 3.6m	16'5" x 11'10"
Bedroom 4	3.7 x 3.1m	12'0" x 10'2"
Bathroom	4.0 x 2.1m	13'1" x 6'11"
FRONTAGE	16.9m	55 ft
AREA	219.0 sq. m.	357 sq. ft.

See page 104 to order this design by Post

HOUSE D-207

An elegant, modern, two-storey residence. The Tudor style shown is full of character and has become quite popular down the years. The larger than normal sitting room acts as a focal point for the ground floor

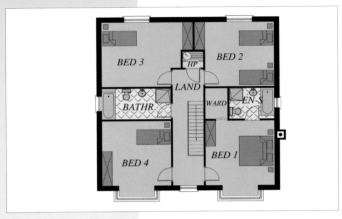

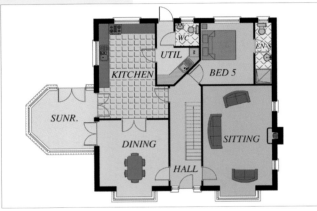

D-207		
Hall	6.1 x 1.8m	20'0" x 5'9"
Dining Room	4.1m x 4.1m	13'5" x 13'5"
Sun Room	3.7 x 3.6m	12'1" x 11'8"
Kitchen	5.8 x 3.3m	19'0" x 10'8"
Utility	2.5 x 2.2m	8'2" x 7'2"
WC	1.4 x 1.4m	4'6"x 4'6"
Sitting Room	6.1 x 4.1m	20'0" x 13'5"
Landing	7.1 x 1.8m	23'3" x 5'9"
Hot Press	1.2 x 1.0m	3'9" x 3'3"
Bedroom 1	4.1 x 3.9m	13'5" x 12'8"
En suite	2.6 x 1.9m	8'5" x 6'2"
Wardrobe	1.9 x 1.3m	6'2" x 4'3"
Bedroom 2	4.1 x 3.9m	13'52 x 12'8"
Bedroom 3	5.4 x 3.9m	17'7" x 12'8"
Bedroom 4	4.1 x 3.9m	13'5" x 12'8"
Bedroom 4	4.1 x 3.9m	13'5" x 12'8"
Bathroom 5	3.8 x 3.1m	12'4" x 10'2"
En suite	3.8 x 1.0m	12'4" x 3'2"
FRONTAGE	10.8m	35 ft
AREA	221.5 sq. m.	2384 sq. ft.

See page 101 for plan prices

HOUSE D-208

A charming dormer bungalow. Houses such as this are commonly used to overcome strict planning height restrictions, where applicable. The inclusion of a rear hall allows the utility area to be kept private.

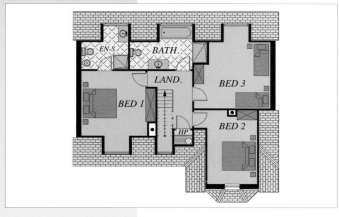

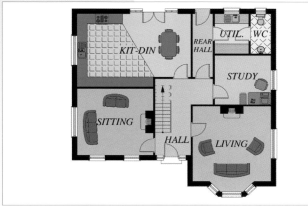

D-208		
Hall	2.1m	6'9"
Sitting Room	4.5 x 4.1m	14'8" x 13'5"
Living Room	4.6 x 4.6m	15'1" x 15'1"
Study	3.3 x 3.0m	10'8" x 9'8"
Kitchen/Dining	6.6 x 4.5m	21'7" x 14'8"
Rear Hall	1.2m	3'9"
Utility	2.0 x 2.4m	6'6" x 7'9"
WC	2.4 x 1.2m	7'9" x 3'9"
Landing	2.1m	6'9"
Bedroom 1	4.4 x 4.0m	14'4" x 13'1"
En suite	2.9 x 2.7m	9'5" x 8'9"
Bedroom 2	4.6 x 3.0m	15'1" x 9'8"
Bedroom 3	4.6 x 4.1m	15'1" x 13'5"
Bathroom	4.6 x 2.3m	15'1" x 7'6"
Hot Press	1.1m x 0.9m	3'6" x 2'10"
FRONTAGE	11.9m	39 ft
AREA	188.8 sq. m.	2030 sq. ft.

HOUSE D-209

A fabulous Georgian style two storey. Header over windows, whether in stone as shown here or alternatively in plaster or brick, look very well. The symmetrical chimneys are a common feature of Georgian architecture

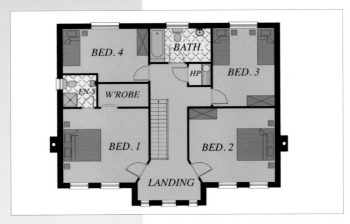

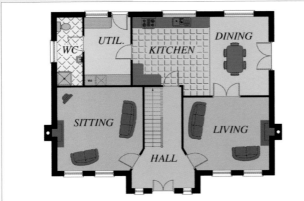

D-209		
Hall	3.4 x 5.7m	11'2" x 18'7"
Living Room	4.6 x 4.1m	15'1" x 13'5"
Sitting Room	4.7 x 4.6m	15'4" x 15'1"
Kitchen/Dining	7.4 x 4.4m	24'3" x 14'4"
Utility	3.8 x 2.5m	12'5" x 8'2"
WC	3.8 x 1.4m	12'5" x 4'6"
Landing	2.3 x 3.4m	7'6" x 11'2"
Bedroom 1	4.6 x 4.1m	15'1" x 13'5"
En suite	1.8 x 1.8m	5'9" x 5'9"
Wardrobe	2.7 x 1.3m	8'9" x 4'3"
Bedroom 2	4.6 x 4.1m	15'1" x 13'5"
Bedroom 3	4.3 x 3.3m	14'1" x 10'8"
Bedroom 4	4.6 x 3.0m	15'1" x 9'8"
Bathroom	3.3 x 1.9m	10'8" x 6'2"
Hot Press	1.2 x 1.2m	3'9" x 3'9"
FRONTAGE	12.1m	40 ft
AREA	205.5 sq. m.	2210 sq. ft.

**Phone
00 353 56
7771300 to order
plans by credit card
from outside the
Republic of Ireland**

HOUSE D-210

A distinctive two-storey structure. The extended porch as shown here has become very popular. The right angle staircase forms the focal point of the main entrance hall.

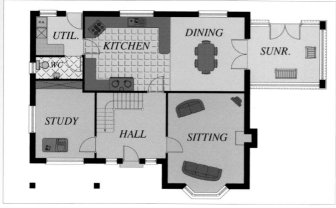

D-210		
Hall	3.6 x 3.7m	11'8" x 12'1"
Sitting Room	5.0 x 4.0m	16'4" x 13'1"
Study	4.3 x 3.1m	14'1" x 10'2"
Sun Room	3.7 x 3.1m	12'1" x 10'2"
Kitchen/Dining	8.5 x 4.1m	27'9" x 13'5"
Utility	2.5 x 2.1m	8'2" x 6'9"
WC	2.5 x 1.2m	8'2" x 3'9"
Landing	5.0 x 3.7m	16'4" x 12'1"
Bedroom 1	4.1 x 4.1m	14'4" x 14'4"
En suite	2.0 x 1.9m	6'6" x 6.2"
Wardrobe	1.9 x 1.1m	6'2" x 3'6"
Bedroom 2	4.3 x 3.0m	14'1" x 9'8"
Bedroom 3	3.7 x 2.6m	12'1" x 8'5"
Bedroom 4	3.6 x 3.1m	11'8" x 10'2"
Bathroom	2.8 x 2.6m	9'2" x 8'5"
Hot Press	1.3 x 1.2m	4'3" x 3'9"
FRONTAGE	11.7m	38 ft
AREA	198.0 sq. m.	2131 sq. ft.

HOUSE D-211

A stunning dormer dwelling. Stone and plaster combine very well indeed to create this fabulous exterior. The large sitting room forms the centrepiece of the ground floor layout and leads directly on to the other key habitable areas.

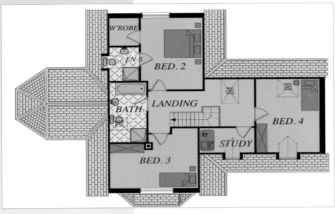

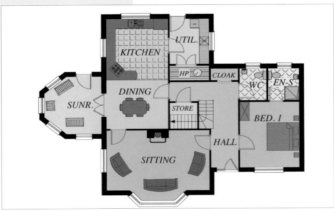

D-211		
Hall	5.6 x 2.4m	18'4" x 7'9"
Cloak	1.7 x 0.7	5'9" x 2'3"
WC	2.1 x 1.7m	6'9" x 5'9"
Sitting Room	6.4 x 3.9m	21'0" x 12'8"
Kitchen/Dining	7.0 x 3.8m	22'10" x 12'5"
Sun Room	3.7 x 3.5m	12'1" x 11'5"
Utility	2.9 x 2.4m	9'5" x 7'9"
Hot Press	2.4 x 0.9m	7'9" x 2'10"
Bedroom 1	4.2 x 3.7m	13'8" x 12'1"
En suite	2.1 x 1.9m	6'9" x 6'2"
Landing	5.8 x 3.0m	19'1" x 9'8"
Bedroom 2	4.6 x 3.4m	15'1" x 11'2"
En suite	2.2 x 1.6m	7'2" x 5'3"
Wardrobe	1.8 x 1.6m	5'9" x 5'3"
Bedroom 3	4.8 x 3.9m	15'8" x 12'8"
Bedroom 4	4.7 x 3.5m	15'4" x 11'5"
Study	3.0 x 1.6m	9'8" x 5'3"
Bathroom	3.8 x 2.0m	12'5" x 6'6"
FRONTAGE	12.6m	41 ft
AREA	208.0 sq. m.	2239 sq. ft.

See page 104 to order this design by Post

HOUSE D-212

An elegant yet practical dormer dwelling. The staircase forms the central feature around the entrance hallway and landing area. A large pantry as shown here has come back into fashion and is useful for many types of storage on the ground floor.

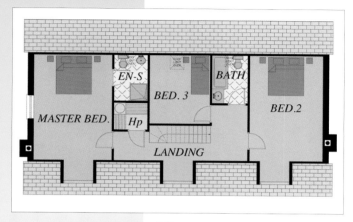

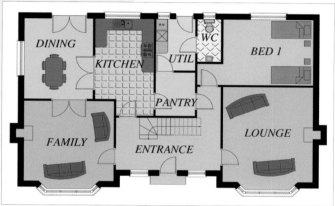

D-212		
Entrance	2.7m	8'9"
Lounge	5.0 x 4.5m	16'4" x 14'8"
Family Room	4.5 x 4.2m	14'8" x 13'8"
Dining Room	4.2 x 3.5m	13'92 x 11'5"
Kitchen	5.1 x 3.0m	16'7" x 9'8"
Pantry	2.3 x 2.0m	7'6" x 6'6"
Utility	2.7 x 2.0m	8'9" x 6'6"
WC	2.2 x 1.2m	7'2" x 3'9"
Bedroom 1	4.5 x 3.4m	14'8" x 11'2"
Landing	2.9m	9'5"
Bedroom 2	5.5 x 3.7m	18'0" x 12'1"
Bedroom 3	3.5 x 3.0m	11'5" x 9'8"
Master Bedroom	5.5 x 3.9m	18'0" x 12'8"
En suite	2.4 x 1.7m	7'9" x 5'6"
Hot Press	1.7 x 1.4m	5'6" x 4'6"
FRONTAGE	15.2m	50 ft
AREA	208.6 sq. m.	2245 sq. ft.

See page 101 for plan prices

HOUSE D-213

A blend of brick and plaster combine very on this superb five-bedroom house. The main habitable areas are easily accessible from each other and the central hallway.

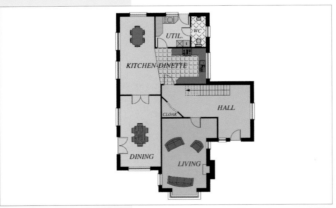

D-213

Hall	7.3 x 3.3m	23'10" x 10'8"
Living Room	5.5 x 3.6m	18'0" x 11'8"
Dining Room	6.1 x 3.3m	20'0" x 10'8"
Kitchen	3.7 x 3.0m	12'1" x 9'8"
Dinette	6.7 x 3.3m	21'10" x 10'8"
Utility	2.8 x 2.6m	9'2" x 8'5"
WC	2.6 x 1.2m	8'5" x 3'9"
Landing	5.9 x 1.8m	19'4" x 5'9"
Bedroom 1	4.6 x 3.4m	15'1" x 11'2"
En suite	2.5 x 2.4m	8'2" x 7'9"
Wardrobe	2.4 x 1.6m	7'9" x 5'3"
Bedroom 2	4.3 x 3.6m	14'1" x 11'8"
Bedroom 3	4.6 x 3.3m	15'1" x 10'8"
Bedroom 4	4.6 x 3.3m	15'1" x 10'8"
Bedroom 5	5.3 x 4.6m	17'4" x 15'1"
Hot Press	2.5 x 2.4m	8'2" x 7'9"
Bathroom	2.6 x 1.6	8'5" x 5'3"
FRONTAGE	11.3m	37 ft
AREA	232.0 sq. m.	2497 sq. ft.

HOUSE D-214

An impressive 4 bedroom residence. Two splayed bay windows to the front rooms throw a lot of light to this area. All four bedrooms are roughly similar in size and can all accommodate double beds with ease.

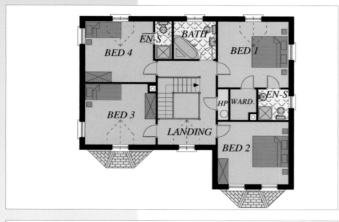

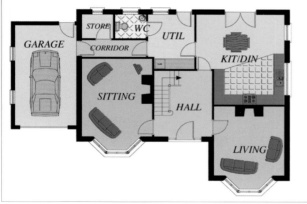

D-214		
Hall	3.9 x 3.3m	12'9" x 10'8"
Sitting Room	4.1 x 4.0m	13'5" x 13'0"
Living Room	4.0 x 4.1m	13'1" x 13'5"
Kitchen/Dining	5.3 x 5.0m	17'4" x 16'4"
Utility	3.2 x 2.6m	10'5" x 8'5"
WC	1.8 x 1.4m	5'9" x 4'6"
Store	1.8 x 1.4m	5'9" x 4'6"
Corridor	1m	3'3"
Landing	1.5m	4'9"
Bedroom 1	4.0 x 3.8m	13'1" x 12'5"
En suite	1.8 x 1.7m	5'9" x 5'6"
Wardrobe	1.8 x 1.4m	5'9" x 4'6"
Bedroom 2	4.0 x 3.6m	13'1" x 11'8"
Bedroom 3	4.0 x 3.5m	13'1" x 11'5"
Bedroom 4	4.0 x 3.5m	13'12 x 11'5"
En suite	2.2 x 0.9m	7'2" x 11'5"
Bathroom	2.4 x 2.2m	7'9" x 7'2"
Hot Press	1.8 x 0.6m	5'9" x 2'10"
Garage	5.9 x 3.5m	19'5" x 11'6"
FRONTAGE - without garage	12.1m	40 ft
AREA	207.7 sq. m.	2236 sq. ft.

HOUSE D-215

A two-storey house full of character. The various rooms in the multi bedroom design can be used for alternative purposes. The hall and landing area form the centrepiece in the main part of the residence.

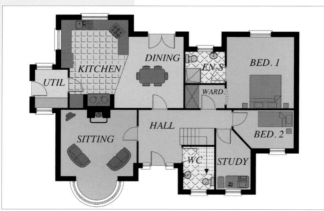

D-215		
Hall	3.2 x 2.5m	10'5" x 8'2"
Study	3.6 x 2.0m	11'8" x 6'6"
WC	2.6 x 1.8m	8'5" x 5'9"
Sitting Room	4.3 x 4.0m	14'1" x 13'1"
Kitchen	5.3 x 3.9m	17'4" x 12'8"
Dining	4.3 x 3.2m	14'1" x 10'5"
Utility	2.3 x 1.9m	7'6" x 6'2"
Bedroom 1	3.9 x 4.3m	12'8" x 14'1"
En suite	2.3 x 1.9m	7'6" x 6'2"
Wardrobe	1.4 x 2.3m	4'6" x 7'6"
Bedroom 2	3.6 x 2.0m	11'8" x 6'6"
Landing	4.8 x 3.9m	15'8" x 12'8"
Bedroom 3	3.7 x 3.9m	21'10" x 12'8"
En suite	2.3 x 1.7m	7'6" x 5'6"
Wardrobe	2.3 x 1.6m	7'6" x 5'3"
Bedroom 4	5.0 x 4.4m	16'4" x 14'4"
Bedroom 5	4.4 x 3.3m	14'4" x 10'8"
Bathroom	3.8 x 2.6m	12'5" x 8'5"
Hot Press	2.5 x 1.2m	8'2" x 3'9"
FRONTAGE	14.1m	46 ft
AREA	223.4 sq. m.	2404 sq. ft.

HOUSE D-216

Two large protrusions dominate the frontage of this imposing one and a half storey residence. The brick bands as shown offer a nice touch, but these may be changed if desired. The large first floor study may be used as an alternative bedroom if desired.

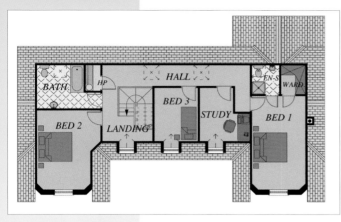

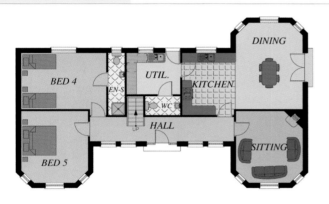

D-216		
Hall	1.5m	4'9"
Kitchen	3.8 x 2.9m	12'5" x 9'5"
Dining	4.7 x 4.0m	15'4" x 13'1"
Utility	3.2 x 2.6m	10'5" x 8'5"
WC	2.0 x 1.2m	6'6" x 3'9"
Sitting Room	4.4 x 4.0m	14'4" x 13'1"
Bedroom 1	5.8 x 3.2m	19'0" x 10'5"
En suite	1.8 x 1.6m	5'9" x 5'3"
Wardrobe	1.8 x 1.4m	5'9" x 4'6"
Bedroom 2	4.9 x 3.8m	16'1" x 12'5"
Bedroom 3	3.3 x 2.6m	10'8" x 8'5"
Bedroom 4	5.1 x 3.5m	16'7" x 11'5"
En suite	2.7 x 1.0m	8'9" x 3'3"
Bedroom 5	4.4 x 4.0m	14'4" x 13'1"
Study	3.3 x 2.0m	10'8" x 6'6"
Hot Press	2.0 x 0.9m	6'6" x 2'10"
Bathroom	2.8 x 2.7m	9'2" x 8'7"
FRONTAGE	17.4m	57 ft
AREA	216.0 sq. m.	2328 sq. ft.

See page 104 to order this design by Post

HOUSE D-217

A surprisingly straightforward dormer dwelling. The balcony is an especially welcome addition. The main feature sitting room/dining room are full of glass and light throughout.

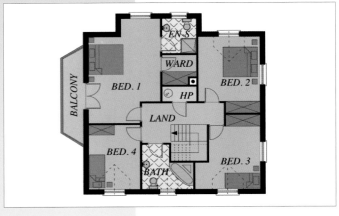

D-216

Hall	3.9 x 1.5m	9'8" x 4'9"
WC	2.2 x 1.6m	7'2" x 5'8"
Study	3.9 x 3.0m	12'8" x 9'8"
Kitchen	3.9 x 3.0m	12'8" x 9'8"
Dining Room	3.4 x 2.6m	11'2" x 8'5"
Sitting Room	4.4 x 6.3m	14'42 x 20'7"
Landing	4.8 x 2.4m	15'82 x 7'9"
Bedroom 1	5.2 x 4.2m	17'12 x 13'8"
En suite	2.1 x 2.0m	6'9" x 6'6"
Wardrobe	2.0 x 1.8m	6.6" x 5'9"
Bedroom 2	4.6 x 3.6m	15'1" x 11'8"
Bedroom 3	4.5 x 3.8m	14'8" x 12'5"
Bedroom 4	3.9 x 3.0m	12'8" x 9'8"
Bathroom	3.0 x 2.7m	9'8" x 8'7"
Hot Press	2.0 x 0.9m	6'6" x 2'10"
Bedroom 5	3.6 x 3.4m	11'8" x 11'2"
FRONTAGE	10.6m	34 ft
AREA	192.1 sq. m.	2068 sq. ft.

Building Contractor or Direct Labour

Can you manage the construction of your dream home or is it better to employ a professional builder? How much money will you save? How much time is involved? All these factors have to be brought into the equation before a decision is made. A large proportion of people who self-build their own home work in the construction industry, or have close relatives who work in the construction industry. They have a head start on ordinary mortals who want to follow this route. In order to help you choose we have listed the advantages and disadvantages of this arrangement below.

Advantages

• A great deal of money can be saved. Some diligent self-builders can make a saving of up to 25 to 30% off a builder's price when doing the job themselves. This office has experience of one very efficient man cutting the cost in half from the sum tendered by building contractors. However, the average for most people generally works out at around to 12 to 16%.

•As with anything else in life, the saving made depends on how much input you are willing to invest in the project. Manual and skilled labour is very expensive and time and effort spent saving on this can result in huge financial benefits.

• Control over building methods. Where a building contractor is employed a huge degree of trust is placed in him with regard to hidden work such as foundations, insulation etc. In the vast majority of cases this trust is more than justified. However, where you feel a personal touch can be helpful on your part on an individual sub contract (e.g. extra insulation in the attic space, deeper window sills, type of floor covering etc.), these can be decided and discussed almost on a day to day basis. You may have a clearer picture of the character of the dwelling as the work progresses.

• There is a terrific amount of self-satisfaction from being directly involved in the construction of your own home.

Pit Falls

• Time, time, time. Basically when you employ a builder you are paying him for the time spent involved in co-ordinating and constructing your house. When you take his place you must be prepared to invest that time yourself in the project. On average the amount of hours spent by self-builders on their own house is around one hour per day, over the entire life span of the building project. This is always staggered and while some weeks require little or no involvement, other crucial time periods (particularly at sub structure or base and second fixing level) can take up enormous amounts of time.

• Patience has to be a virtue. The average length of a standard dwelling construction is in or around 5/7 months, this increases to 9/10 months on average for direct labour but can increase quite dramatically to a year or more. Obviously while the construction is under way you are paying the mortgage and quite possibly renting your current home at the same time, all of which must be borne in mind.

Insurance on the building and building site

• Technically when a building contractor agrees to construct your home he has sole jurisdiction over the entire building site, including the important issue in modern day life of insurance. Some, but not many, insurance companies provide 'all in' insurance for direct labour type of jobs, but this has increased at least three fold in the last four years. Shop around for the best and ideally have an independent broker check the small print if possible.

Co-ordination of the building trades and your telephone bill!

• Generally speaking the longer a house progresses the more complicated it becomes. For second fixing such as electrician, plumber, plasterer etc., a lot of co-operation and mutual help is required. You must be the supervisor in this case. Time keeping by tradesmen can be notoriously fickle and the normal way to maintain progress is through phoning to arrange and rearrange appointments.

Remember if a plasterer has to re do work because an electrical item was not in place he shall charge double.

Summary

Speak to friends, relations and they can give you a good idea of what can be involved with either option. Our office always recommends a building contractor but ensure he is registered, recommended, and most importantly available

when stated. On the other hand building by direct labour can be a most rewarding if time consuming experience. Make up your mind and stick with the decision in either case.

Section E

House Designs from 2501 sq. ft. upwards.

TIP: A layer of plywood (min. 12.5mm) under a timber floor finish to upper storeys can really help to deaden impact sound. The plywood should be screwed not nailed. Alternatively a layer of plasterboard may be used. Additionally incorporate 4-6 inches of a high density sound insulation between joists to lessen the effect of airborne sound.

See page 104 to order this design by Post

HOUSE E-201

A superb yet straightforward dwelling design. The feature staircase in the entrance hallway acts as a centrepiece for the entire residence. The enormous attached garage on the right may be used both for car and storage.

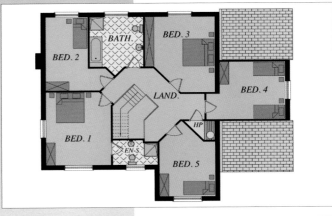

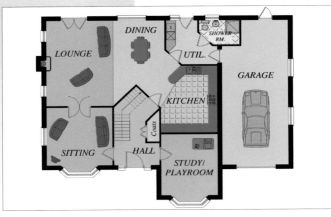

E-201		
Hall	3.9 x 2.9m	12'8" x 9'5"
Coats	2.1 x 0.8m	6'9" x 2'6"
Study/Playroom	4.2 x 3.6m	13'8" x 11'8"
Sitting Room	4.2 x 3.9m	13'8" x 12'8"
Kitchen	4.5 x 3.6m	14'8" x 11'8"
Lounge/Dining	7.5 x 5.9m	24'6" x 19'4"
Utility	3.2 x 3.0m	10'5" x 9'8"
Shower Room	2.5 x 1.6m	8'2" x 5'3"
Landing	1.6m	5'3"
Bedroom 1	4.8 x 4.2m	15'8" x 13'8"
En suite	1.6 x 2.9m	5'3" x 9'8"
Bedroom 2	4.9 x 2.7m	16'1" x 8'9"
Bedroom 3	5.0 x 4.5m	16'4" x 14'8"
Bedroom 4	4.2 x 3.8m	13'8" x 12'5"
Bedroom 5	3.6 x 3.6m	11'8" x 11'8"
Hot Press	2.0 x 1.2m	6'6" x 3'9"
Bathroom	3.4 x 3.3m	16'1" x 8'9"
Garage	9.8 x 4.2m	32'1" x 13'8"
FRONTAGE	16.0m	52 ft
AREA	293. sq. m.	3154 sq. ft.

Log on to Houseplans.ie to order plans and to quote for changes.

HOUSE E-202

The stunning exterior of this residence ties in perfectly with the impressive rooms both on the ground and first floor internally. The skylight to the ridge is an attractive effect, offering light to the landing area. The recessed front door allows for a superb arch effect over the landing area window.

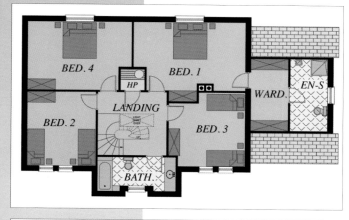

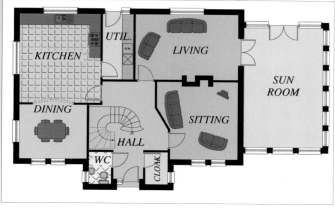

E-202		
Hall	1.4m	4'6"
WC	1.8 x 1.2m	5'9" x 3'9"
Cloak	1.8 x 1.2m	5'9" x 3'9"
Sitting Room	4.3 x 4.3m	14'1" x 14'1"
Dining Room	3.6 x 3.0m	11'8" x 9'8"
Kitchen	4.9 x 4.3m	16'1" x 14'1"
Utility	3.6 x 1.6m	11'8" x 5'3"
Living Room	5.4 x 3.6m	17'7" x 11'8"
Sun Room	6.6 x 4.2m	21'7" x 13'8"
Landing	1.2m	3'9"
Bedroom 1	6.0 X 3.8m	19'7"x 12'5"
Wardrobe	4.0 x 2.0m	13'1" x 6'6"
En suite	4.0 x 2.0m	13'1" x 6'6"
Bedroom 2	4.1 x 3.7m	13'5" x 12'1"
Bedroom 3	4.1 x 4.1m	13'52 x 13'5"
Bedroom 4	5.6 x 3.8m	18'4" x 12'5"
Hotpress	1.3 x 1.2m	4'3" x 3'11"
Bathroom	4.2 x 4.9m	13'8" x 6'2"
FRONTAGE	16.7m	55ft
AREA	245.4 sq. m.	2640 sq. ft.

73

HOUSE E-203

A two-storey bay, side living room and over hanging porch are just one of the eye catching features on the exterior of this family residence. The main structure is two-storey in height while the dormer section on the right-hand side contrasts perfectly with this height. The upstairs bathroom is at once both spacious and easily accessible from the other rooms to this area.

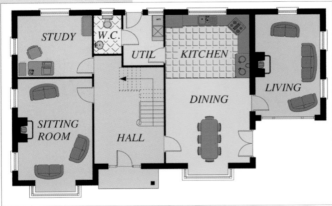

E-203

Hall	6.1 x 3.6m	20'0" x 11'8"
Sitting Room	5.5 x 3.9m	18'0" x 12'8"
Study	3.9 x 3.3m	12'8" x 10'8"
Kitchen/Dining	8.0 x 4.4m	26'2" x 14'4"
Living Room	5.4 x 3.4m	17'7" x 11'2"
Utility	2.7 x 2.1m	8'9" x 6'9"
WC	1.7 x 1.4m	5'6" x 4'6"
Landing	13.6 x 6.5m	11'5" x 21'3"
Master Bedroom	5.2 x 4.4m	17'1" x 14'4"
En Suite	3.4 x 2.3m	11'2" x 7'6"
Wardrobe	3.4 x 2.6m	11'2" x 8'5"
Bedroom 2	8.1 x 2.7m	26'6" x 8'9"
Bedroom 3	3.9 x 3.1m	12'8" x 10'2"
Bedroom 4	3.9 x 3.1m	12'8" x 10'2"
Bathroom	3.9 x 2.5m	12'5" x 8'2"
Hot Press	2.7 x 1.5m	8'9" x 4'9"
FRONTAGE	16.4m	54 ft
AREA	247.1 sq. m.	2660 sq. ft.

HOUSE E-204

This spacious dormer offers 5 large bedrooms together with a living and sitting room. The porch area to the front also offers character along with acting as a weather barrier. As can be seen the Dutch hips on the roof combine very well with the hipped dormer windows.

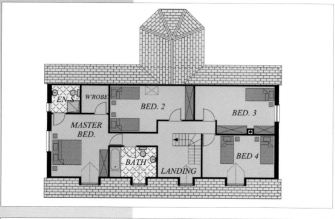

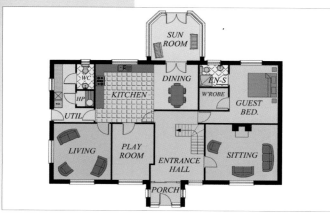

E-204		
Entrance Hall	5.2 x 3.4m	17'1" x 11'2"
Sitting Room	5.0 x 4.2m	16'4" x 13'8"
Play Room	4.2 x 2.9m	13'8" x 9'5"
Living Room	4.2 x 4.0m	13'8" x 13'1"
Sun room	3.4 x 3.4m	11'2" x 11'2"
Dining Room	3.4 x 3.1m	11'2" x 10'2"
Kitchen	4.1 x 4.4m	13'3" x 14'4"
Utility	4.4 x 1.5m	14'4" x 4'9"
WC	1.9 x 1.2m	6'2" x 3'9"
Hot Press	1.2 x 1.2m	3'9" x 3'9"
Guest Bedroom	4.4 x 3.4m	14'4" x 11'2"
En suite	2.0 x 1.7m	6'6" x 5'6"
Wardrobe	2.0 x 1.8m	6'6" x 5'6"
Landing	4.1 x 3.0m	13'5" x 9'8"
Master Bedroom	4.5 x 4.0m	14'8" x 13'1"
En suite	2.0 x 2.0m	6'6" x 6'6"
Wardrobe	1.9 x 2.0m	6'2" x 6'6"
Bedroom 2	5.9 x 3.4m	19'4" x 11'2"
Bedroom 3	5.6 x 3.5m	18'4" x 11'5"
Bedroom 4	5.1 x 3.1m	16'7" x 10'2"
Bathroom	3.3 x 2.2m	10'8" x 7'2"
FRONTAGE	16.5m	54ft
AREA	258.8 sq. m.	2786 sq. ft.

See page 101 for plan prices

HOUSE E-205

An extended porch welcomes guests and homeowners alike to relax in this five bedroom, two-storey residence. The long frontage gives this dwelling a stately effect. A cloakroom as shown adjacent to the main lobby is a useful addition and provides great storage space.

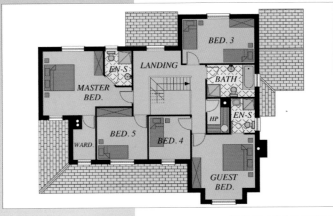

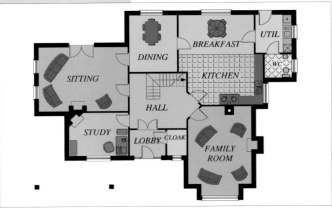

E-205		
Lobby	2.4 x 1.8m	7'9" x 5'9"
Cloak	1.8 x 1.3m	5'9" x 4'3"
Hall	3.8 x 3.8m	12'5" x 12'5"
Study	3.9 x 3.0m	12'8" x 9'8"
Sitting Room	5.9 x 4.4m	19'4" x 14'4"
Dining Room	3.9 x 3.2m	12'8" x 10'5"
Kitchen/Breakfast	6.2 x 5.0m	20'3" x 16'4"
Utility	2.6 x 2.4m	8'5" x 7'9"
WC	1.8 x 1.6m	5'9" x 5'3"
Family Room	5.4 x 4.2m	17'7" x 13'8"
Landing	1.7m	5'6"
Master Bedroom	4.4 x 4.1m	14'4"x 13'5"
En suite	2.4 x 1.8m	7'9" x 5'9"
Wardrobe	3.0 x 1.5m	9'8" x 4'9"
Guest Bedroom	4.2 x 3.7m	13'8"x 12'1"
En suite	2.4 x 1.6m	7'9" x 5'3"
Bedroom 3	4.8 x 3.1m	15'8" x 10'2"
Bedroom 4	3.0 x 2.8m	9'8" x 9'2"
Bedroom 5	3.6 x 3.3m	11'8" x 10'8"
Bathroom	3.2 x 2.2m	10'5" x 7'2"
Hot Press	2.4 x 1.5m	7'9" x 4'9"
FRONTAGE	14.8m	49 ft
AREA	263.6 sq. m.	2837 sq. ft.

See page 104 to order this design by Post

HOUSE E-206

Here is a family home with plenty of living space. The peaked roofs on the façade have an eye catching pleasant appeal. A spacious utility room as shown here is becoming increasingly essential in today's busy world.

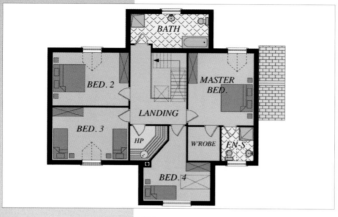

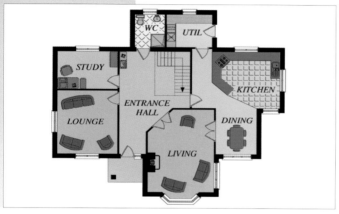

E-206		
Entrance Hall	7.1 x 4.6m	23'3" x 15'1"
Living Room	5.8 x 4.3m	19'0" x 14'1"
Lounge	4.4 x 3.9m	14'4" x 12'8"
Study	3.9 x 2.5m	12'8" x 8'2"
Kitchen	5.7 x 3.9m	18'7" x 12'8"
Dining	3.2 x 2.6m	10'5" x 8'5"
Utility	2.9 x 2.2m	9'5" x 7'2"
WC	2.2 x 1.9m	7'2" x 6'2"
Landing	4.7 x 3.6m	15'4" x 11'8"
Master bedroom	4.7 x 4.2m	15'2 x 13'8"
En suite	2.2 x 2.0m	7'2" x 6'6"
Wardrobe	2.2 x 2.0m	7'2" x 6'6"
Bedroom 2	4.9 x 3.5m	16'1" x 11'5"
Bedroom 3	4.9 x 3.5m	16'1" x 11'5"
Bedroom 4	4.9 x 4.3m	16'1" x 14'1"
Hot Press	2.3 x 2.4m	7'6" x 7'9"
FRONTAGE	15.0m	49ft
AREA	238.8 sq. m.	2570 sq. ft.

Log on to
Houseplans.ie
to order plans and
to quote for
changes.

HOUSE E-207

An imposing elegant house. A stone finish as suggested here can cut down on the high cost of a finish around the entire building, but nonetheless provide the desired effect. The straightforward layout on both floors is tremendously effective.

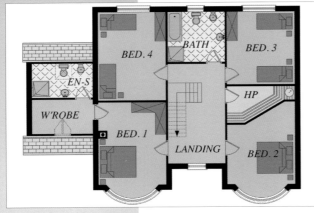

E-207

Hall	4.6 x 3.2m	15'1" x 10'5"
Study	3.3 x 3.8m	10'8" x 12'5"
Sitting	5.8 x 3.8m	19'0" x 12'5"
Sun Room	5.5 x 3.4m	18'0" x 11'2"
Dining	4.0 x 3.8m	13'0" x 12'5"
Kitchen/Breakfast	7.1 x 4.0m	23'3" x 13'1"
Utility	2.4 x 2.3m	7'9" x 7'6"
WC	2.4 x 1.4m	7'9" x 4'6"
Landing	4.6 x 3.2m	15'0" x 10'5"
Bedroom 1	4.7 x 3.8m	15'4" x 12'5"
En suite	2.0 x 3.4 m	6'6" x 11'2"
Wardrobe	3.4 x 1.9m	11'2" x 6'2"
Bedroom 2	5.6 x 3.8m	18'4" x 12'5"
Bedroom 3	4.2 x 3.8m	13'8" x 12'5"
Bedroom 4	5.1 x 3.8m	16'7" x 12'5"
Bathroom	3.2 x 2.9m	10'5" x 9'5"
Hot Press	3.8 x 2.1m	10'5" x 6'9"
FRONTAGE	15.1m	50ft
AREA	251.8 sq. m.	2710 sq. ft.

**Phone
00 353 56
7771300 to order
plans by credit card
from outside the
Republic of Ireland**

HOUSE E-208

*Intricate rooflines, together with a varied assortment of windows,
combine to create this magnificent family home. The front elevation
is magnificent and in particular the curved arch over the central
entrance doorway. The ground floor boasts two large living rooms.*

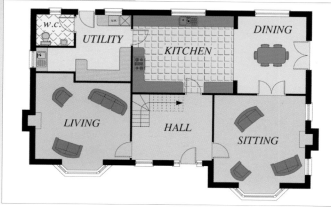

E-208

Hall	4.2 x 3.6m	13'8" x 11'8"
Living	5.0 x 4.2m	16'4" x 13'8"
Sitting	4.8 x 4.8m	15'8" x 15'8"
Dining	4.2 x 3.7m	13'8" x 12'1"
Kitchen	5.4 x 4.2m	17'7" x 13'8"
Utility	3.1 x 2.9m	10'2" x 9'5"
WC	2.0 x 1.7m	6'6" x 5'6"
Landing	4.7 x 4.2m	15'4" x 13'5"
Bedroom 1	4.8 x 4.8m	15'8" x 15'8"
Wardrobe	2.1 x 1.9m	6'9" x 6'2"
En suite	2.0 x 1.9m	6'6" x 6'2"
Bedroom 2	5.3 x 4.2m	17'4" x 13'8"
Bedroom 3	4.3 x 3.5m	14'1" x 11'5"
Bedroom 4	5.0 x 3.5m	16'4" x 11'5"
Bathroom	3.1 x 3.1m	10'2" x 10'2"
FRONTAGE	14.8m	49ft
AREA	240.8 sq. m.	2592 sq. ft.

HOUSE E-209

An impressive five bedroom house with many features. A combination of styles is amalgamated in this terrific design. The kitchen to the rear acts as a focal point for the entire ground floor.

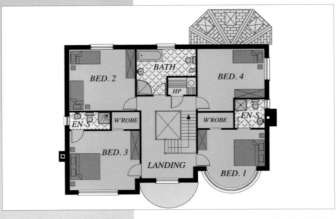

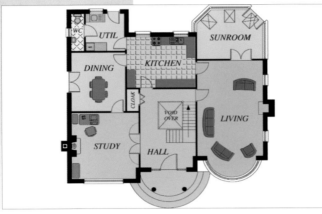

E-209		
Hall	5.6 x 3.8m	18'4" x 12'5"
Cloak	1.5 x 0.8m	4'9" x 2'6"
Living	6.7 x 4.5m	21'10" x 14'8"
Sun Room	4.5 x 3.5m	14'8" x 11'5"
Study	4.7 x 4.6m	15'4" x 15'1"
Dining	4.1 x 3.7m	13'5" x 12'1"
Kitchen	4.7 x 3.6m	15'4" x 11'8"
Utility	2.6 x 2.5m	8'5" x 8'2"
WC	2.7 x 0.9m	8'8" x 2'11"
Landing	5.6 x 3.6m	18'4" x 11'8"
Bathroom	4.0 x 3.1m	13'1" x 10'2"
Hot Press	1.8 x 1.2m	5'9" x 3' 9"
Bedroom 1	4.5 x 2.5m	14'8" x 8' 2"
En suite	2.0 x 2.0	6'6" x 6'6"
Wardrobe	2.4 x 1.0m	7'9" x 3'3"
Bedroom 2	4.5 x 4.3m	14'8" x 14'1"
Bedroom 3	4.7 x 4.1m	15'4" x 13'5"
En suite	2.7 x 1.2m	8'9" x 3'9"
Wardrobe	1.9 x 1.2m	6'2" x 3'9"
Bedroom 4	4.5 x 4.3m	14'8" x 14'1"
FRONTAGE	13.7m	45 ft
AREA	257.5 sq. m.	2772 sq. ft.

See page 101 for plan prices

HOUSE E-210

A very spacious, tasteful two storey house. A sunroom to the rear is a very common feature nowadays. The overall effect is Georgian in style, especially the windows and quoin stones as suggested in this image.

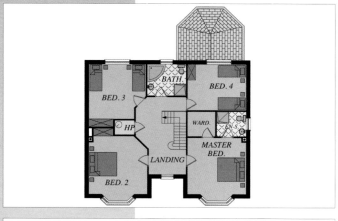

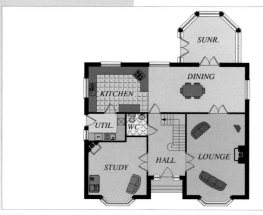

E-210

Entrance Hall	4.8 x 2.7m	15'8" x 8'9"
Study	4.3 x 4.0m	14'1" x 13'1"
Lounge	6.3 x 4.3m	20'7" x 14'1"
Kitchen/Dining	11.6 x 3.5m	38'0" x 11'5"
Utility	2.7 x 2.1m	8'9" x 6'9"
WC	1.5 x 1.5m	4'9" x 4'9"
Sun Room	3.9 x 3.5m	12'8" x 11'5"
Landing	5.9 x 3.7m	19'4" x 12'1"
Master Bedroom	4.3 x 4.3m	14'1" x 14'1"
En suite	2.2 x 19.m	7'2" x 6'2"
Wardrobe	2.1 x 1.9m	6'9" x 6'2"
Bedroom 2	5.0 x 4.3m	16'4" x 14'1"
Bedroom 3	4.8 x 4.2m	15'8" x 13'8"
Bedroom 4	4.3 x 3.5m	14'1" x 11'5"
Bathroom	2.9 x 2.4m	9'5" x 7'9"
Hot Press	1.1 x 1.5m	3'6" x 4'9"
FRONTAGE	12.2m	40ft
AREA	236 sq. m.	2540 sq. ft.

See page 104 to order this design by Post

HOUSE E-211

Symmetry and style colour the façade of this elegant four-bedroom family home. The feature kitchen/dining area to the rear contrasts perfectly with the more formal drawing and dining rooms towards the front area. The overall effect is Georgian, especially with the arch over the front doorway and the columns to the porch in front.

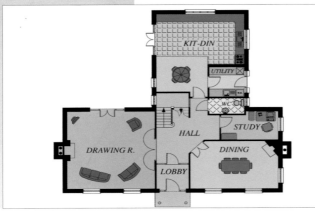

E-211		
Lobby	1.9 x 2.2m	6'2" x 7'2"
Hall	4.3 x 3.5m	14'1" x 11'5"
Drawing	6.0 x 6.0m	19'7" x 19'7"
Dining	6.0 x 3.7m	19'7" x 12'1"
Study	3.9 x 2.2m	12'8" x 7'2"
WC	1.2 x 2.4m	3'9" x 7'9"
Utility	2.4 x 2.3m	7'9" x 7'6"
Kitchen	6.0 x 6.0m	19'7" x 19'7"
Landing	5.4 x 2.4m	17'7" x 7'9"
Master Bedroom	6.0 x 4.9m	19'7" x 16'1"
En suite	1.0 x 3.0m	3'3" x 9'8"
Wardrobe	3.0 x 1.0m	9'8" x 3'3"
Bedroom 2	3.6 x 5.0m	11'8" x 16'4"
En suite	1.8 x 1.8m	5'9" x 5'9"
Wardrobe	1.8 x 0.8m	5'9" x 2'6"
Bedroom 3	2.6 x 6.0m	8'5" x 19'7"
Bedroom 4	3.3 x 5.3m	10'8" x 17'4"
En suite	1.5 x 2.4m	5'3" x 7'9"
Hot Press	1.6 x 1.4m	5'3" x 4'6"
Bathroom	3.2 x 2.3m	10'5" x 7'6"
FRONTAGE	15.0m	49ft
AREA	262 sq. m.	2820 sq. ft.

Mortgage Tips

Where there's a will there's a way. When you first started dreaming of that holiday of a lifetime, or your first car you never thought you'd do it. But chances are, you made it. It can be the same with your first home. With some careful planning and cash-flow management you can have it all – own your very own place and still enjoy a great lifestyle.

Q: I want to buy my own home – where do I start?

A: Before you start you need to know how far your purse strings will stretch to juggle all your lifestyle needs, including your own place. First, make a note of all your current expenses – how much do you spend a month on going out? – It all mounts up. List your savings and any other personal sources of funds too.

Next you should come in and chat to a mortgage advisor. You need to find someone who has a track record of providing excellent advice on a personal level and someone you can trust – after all, this is probably the biggest purchase of your life so far.

First Time Buyers are the most significant segment of mortgage borrowers at the bank, accounting for 30% of the value of new mortgage lending.

Many institutions will assign a personal mortgage advisor to act as a project manager for the whole home purchasing experience and to help you achieve what's most important to you. This makes the process as stress-free as possible, convenient and even enjoyable. You can get mortgage approval up-front too. Once your advisor gives you a ballpark figure for your price range, you can get down to serious house-hunting.

Q: Prices are so high these days, how will I ever be able to afford my own home?

A: It's true that house prices in Ireland have seen unprecedented growth in the last decade but the market has changed too. Many institutions now offer First Time Buyers 92% mortgages and more – that means you would only have to put up 8% or less of the purchase price of your home to secure the deal. Use this offer to your advantage.

Q: Even if I get a mortgage how can I ever afford to kit out my house?

A: There are lots of costs to think about: legal fees, alarms and décor such as wooden floors, furniture, cookers and fridges – it takes everybody months to finish a home. But there is help at hand. Most banks and building societies offer First Time Buyers a pre-approved personal loan of up to €25,000 and you can take up to five years for repayment.

Overdraft facilities at current low mortgage rates should be availed of to help you get over the initial hump of expenses. You may even have offers of a home maintenance helpline with contacts for all kinds of services - plumbers, electricians etc. All you'll have to do is decorate.

Q: What other costs kick in and how will I cope?

A: When it's your first time buying, costs seem to jump out from everywhere. Don't panic. There are several deals to help you through. Firstly, home and life insurance – you cannot buy a home without them. Offers such as three months' free home insurance, an insurance hotline and advice on how to choose the right life policy for you are available.

You'll also need to cover yourself if your income changes – if you feel that your current income could be threatened then you should consider mortgage repayment cover.

If your circumstances change, as they do, and you need flexible repayment terms, most institutions provide low start or deferred payment mortgages and mortgage breaks for those costly times such as new baby arrivals, weddings or dream holidays.

Whatever your situation, your lender will provide you with short- and long-term financial advice and help.

Q: So what is my next step?

A: Call into your nearest broker or institution early on in the house building process for a friendly chat with a mortgage advisor – it's your first home so get it without breaking the bank!

Useful website:

www.oasis.gov.ie/housing and click on Buying a home.

Jargon you'll need to know...

LTV – Loan to Value. This is the percentage of the purchase price or value of a property that a lender is prepared to offer you. Eg. Bank of Ireland offers 92% LTV, meaning you only need to provide 8% of the purchase price up-front as a deposit.

Snag list – when buying a brand new home the builders will require you to inspect the property before you agree it's ready for purchase. You draw up a list of items that are either unfinished, missing, or sub-standard.

Stamp duty – a government tax that you the buyer must pay if you purchase a second-hand home.

The Closing – the final stage in your purchase where your solicitor meets with the other side's solicitor to finish the remaining paperwork and hand you the keys. Then you can pop the champagne!

Article kindly supplied by Bank of Ireland mortgage services. Website: www.boi.ie and click on Personal Banking and Buying a home

The mortgage that takes care of everything.

A mortgage from Bank of Ireland means you can relax and just leave it all to us. We've designed a mortgage package that lets you buy your house, and then helps you turn it into a home. Your personal mortgage adviser is with you all the way and will guide you through the process, making sure you avoid potential pitfalls. A quick glance at some of the benefits will tell you that this is so much more than just a mortgage. It's the mortgage that thinks of everything, so you don't have to.

More than just a mortgage.

- We offer you up to 92% of the value of the house*.

- Upfront mortgage approval that ensures you can proceed with confidence.

- A Gold Advantage credit card (optional).

- Fast track life & medical insurance# – arrange your appointment when and where it suits you between 8am-8pm.

- A range of flexible repayment options.

- A pre-approved personal loan to turn your house into a home (optional).

- An overdraft to help manage day-to-day bills (optional).

- Efficient home insurance claims process with dedicated phone line.

1890 365 345

www.boi.ie/mortgages

Bank of Ireland

Personal Banking

Section G

Garages

TIP: North-east or north-west facing sites are generally considered best. This allows the main rooms such as kitchen/dining/sitting to be located towards the rear for privacy and also have the benefit of direct sunlight.

GARAGE G-201

A straightforward and practical layout. Windows as shown on either side offer terrific light throughout the area.

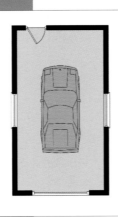

G-201

7.2m x 3.8m / 23'7" x 12'6"

Area: 27.4 sq. m. / 295 sq. ft.

See page 101 for plan prices

GARAGE G-202

This is an alternative on the previous design. The door on the side as shown is the most popular and most common way of entering a garage area.

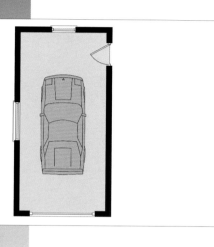

G-202	
	7.0m x 3.3m. / 23'0" x 10'10"
Area:	23.1 sq. m. / 249 sq. ft.

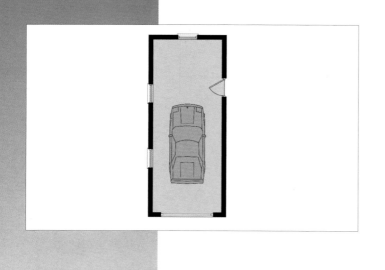

GARAGE G-203

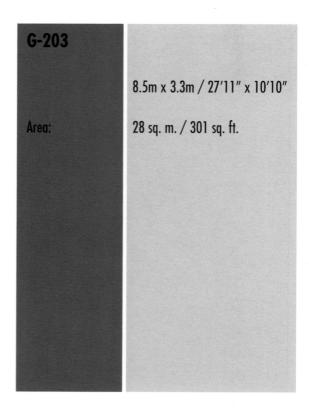

This layout can sort the problem for the many people who cannot decide between sheltering the car and using the garage for storage. This design solves both problems.

G-203

8.5m x 3.3m / 27'11" x 10'10"

Area: 28 sq. m. / 301 sq. ft.

See page 104 to order this design by Post

**Phone
00 353 56
7771300 to order
plans by credit card
from outside the
Republic of Ireland**

GARAGE G-204

An attractive, practical two car garage. With the extra width as shown it is possible to utilise effectively the attic space over this area.

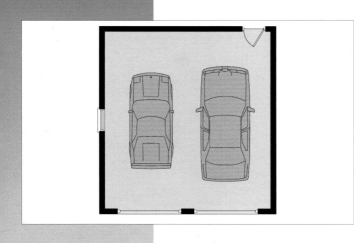

G-204

7.2m x 6.5m / 23'7" x 21'4"

Area:

46.8 sq. m. / 503 sq. ft.

Log on to
Houseplans.ie
to order plans and
to quote for
changes.

GARAGE G-205

Room both for the car and storage! Extra space such as shown here can often be used by the DIY enthusiast as workspace.

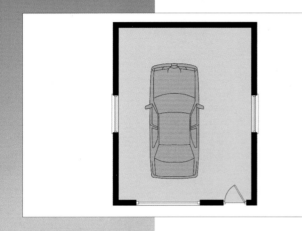

G-205	
	7.0m x 5.2m / 23'0" x 17'1"
Area:	36.4 sq. m. / 392 sq. ft.

See page 101 for plan prices

GARAGE G-206

Something with a difference! The space adjoining the main garage may be used for storage of fuel for example.

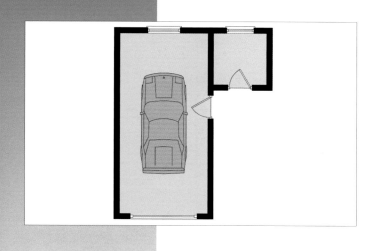

G-206	
	7.0m x 3.3m / 23'0" x 10'10"
Area:	23.1 sq. m. / 249 sq. ft.
Storage:	2.0m x 1.9m / 6'6" x 6'7"
Area:	3.9 sq. m. / 41 sq. ft.

Planning Permission (R.O.I)

The following are a list of the items required by each Local Authority in the Republic of Ireland, in order to lodge an official planning application. However, it is always advisable to seek advice, either directly from the planner in your relevant area, or alternatively, the Local County Development Plan or similar publication.

Additionally, some extra information which might aid a planning officer to favour your application is always a good idea, e.g. details of family involvement in the area, business interests etc., and these can often be submitted as an attached hand written or typed note. See Page 95

1. Signed and fully completed **application form.**

2. **Newspaper notice** as shown in the local/national paper. 2 copies. *See your local authorities guidelines*

3. **Site Notice** which should be dated within the 2 weeks prior to making the application. The site notice should be printed or written legibly on a white background and affixed to A4 rigid material and weatherproofed. 2 copies.

4. 6 copies of sections, elevations and **plans** of your house. Each copy to be in metric scale of not less than 1:200, however, we provide the planning drawings at a larger scale of 1:100. *See your local authorities guidelines.*

5. 6 copies of the building **specification** of your house. This involves notes about the materials to be used in the dwelling, and in particular the finishes, i.e. roof finish, wall finish etc. (as we provide).

6. 6 copies of a **site layout plan.** Minimum scale 1:500, which should show the entire site and any landscaping, driveways, septic tanks, boreholes, north point etc, involved in the site or surrounding sites. Also include some details of the relevant "sight lines", which basically are the visible distances which can be seen as you drive out of the site onto the public roadway. Very important to planners!

7. **Percolation/water table test results,** where a private effluent treatment system (i.e. septic tank), is to be used. It is important to note that different Local Authorities have varied requirements for this test, e.g. some authorities carry out the test themselves and charge a fee, some Local Authorities require the tester to have a certain level of Professional Indemnity Insurance.

8. **Planning Fee.** This currently stands at €65.00 per dwelling. However, this varies if, for example: an existing building is to be demolished, stables are to be constructed, outline permission has already been granted. *See your local authorities guidelines.*

9. 6 copies of the **Site Location Map** scale 1:1000 in built up areas/1:2500 in all other areas. This should easily identify the position of your site in relation to the surrounding area (in red). Don't forget such important items as north sign, ordnance survey number etc.

looking into the future...

We supply a professional 3D illustration service to both architects and developers. Both our experience and command of the latest technology give us our competitive edge. All illustrations in this brochure have been created by our team and display our abilities in the 3D illustration market.

3D ILLUSTRATION & ARCHITECTURAL VISUALISATION   **T** 051 386949 . **E** info@ah-art.org . **W** www.ah-art.org

It can take up to ten working days to receive unaltered plans/specifications from us in Ireland after placing your order.

Allow some extra time where alterations are required.

Local Need/Area Association

Most Local Authority Development Plans currently require what is called a local need requirement in certain areas. This fundamentally means that in what is considered a sensitive area, only people from the area or with strong connections to the area may be allowed planning permission. Although this is not written down as an essential requirement of your planning application in such circumstances we strongly recommend these details be included with your application.

How to convey such information can be quite difficult and for your convenience please find below a typical type of letter which may be hand written or type

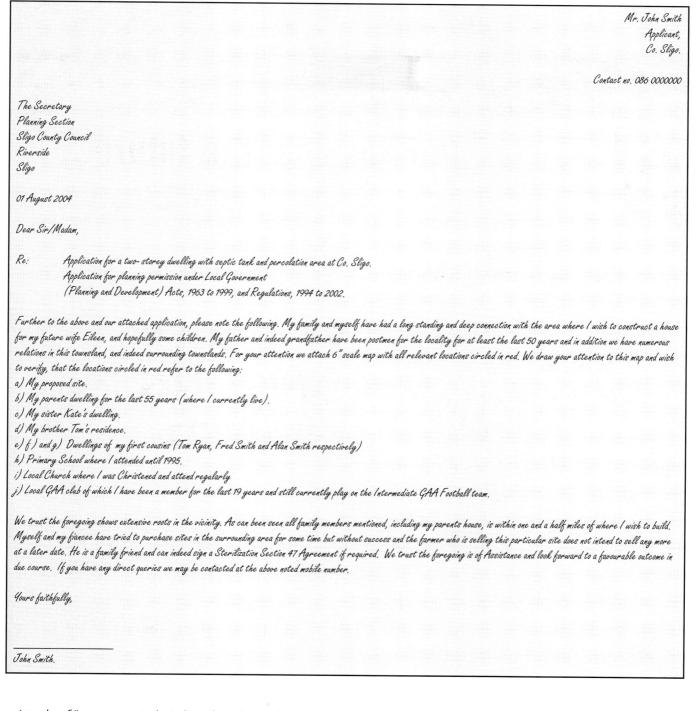

Mr. John Smith
Applicant,
Co. Sligo.

Contact no. 086 0000000

The Secretary
Planning Section
Sligo County Council
Riverside
Sligo

01 August 2004

Dear Sir/Madam,

Re: Application for a two-storey dwelling with septic tank and percolation area at Co. Sligo.
        Application for planning permission under Local Government
        (Planning and Development) Acts, 1963 to 1999, and Regulations, 1994 to 2002.

Further to the above and our attached application, please note the following. My family and myself have had a long standing and deep connection with the area where I wish to construct a house for my future wife Eileen, and hopefully some children. My father and indeed grandfather have been postmen for the locality for at least the last 50 years and in addition we have numerous relations in this townsland, and indeed surrounding townslands. For your attention we attach 6" scale map with all relevant locations circled in red. We draw your attention to this map and wish to verify, that the locations circled in red refer to the following:

a) My proposed site.
b) My parents dwelling for the last 55 years (where I currently live).
c) My sister Kate's dwelling.
d) My brother Tom's residence.
e) f) and g) Dwellings of my first cousins (Tom Ryan, Fred Smith and Alan Smith respectively)
h) Primary School where I attended until 1995.
i) Local Church where I was Christened and attend regularly
j) Local GAA club of which I have been a member for the last 19 years and still currently play on the Intermediate GAA Football team.

We trust the foregoing shows extensive roots in the vicinity. As can been seen all family members mentioned, including my parents house, is within one and a half miles of where I wish to build. Myself and my fiancee have tried to purchase sites in the surrounding area for some time but without success and the farmer who is selling this particular site does not intend to sell any more at a later date. He is a family friend and can indeed sign a Sterilization Section 47 Agreement if required. We trust the foregoing is of Assistance and look forward to a favourable outcome in due course. If you have any direct queries we may be contacted at the above noted mobile number.

Yours faithfully,

_____
John Smith.

Attach a 6" map as stated, circling the relevant locations with a colour pen. If you have met the planner in a pre-planning clinic you may mention him by name on the letter. Remember don't leave out any relevant information and if you happen to be a farmer or part-time farmer such information can also be advantageous.

Design Alterations

The following pages show how designs throughout this book can be altered to suit individual needs and tastes.

MK Home Design offers you the unique opportunity, if so desired of altering the finishes shown in this book, to suit your site or indeed your personal preferences. We have taken a design at random, House B-210, and show how a dwelling can be transformed with some thought and imagination.

In addition, it may be necessary to "flip over" or mirror the plans as shown in order to locate the key habitable areas: kitchen, dining etc. on the sunny side of the site. Again, this can be done free of charge. If your finish differs from that shown in our 3D image, please mark any changes legibly and clearly on the order form on page 104, or state clearly to our office when ordering by credit card. Be sure to include any important features such as arches over windows, plaster reveals etc., etc.

We begin below by having house B-210 (shown on page 46), flipped over and continue on the following pages with just some of the choices available.

So, in addition to finishes the layout of your chosen design may be modified. Again, you may ring or office for advice and a quotation of any extra cost involved. Minor customisation is free of charge. Alternatively, photocopy the page, mark the desired items to be changed clearly, together with your contact details, and we will get right back to you.

Always bear in mind that increasing the size of a dwelling adds to the construction cost.

House B-210 Mirror Image

It's all go!

Now is the time to make sure
your next building project is up to spec.
With the new Building Insulation
Regulations now fully in force,
go to your local merchant and check out
the Aerobord Platinum range, the new silver-grey
colour High Performance insulation board
that puts you in the driving seat.

Aerobord Platinum.
Products of the future built on the Past.

Outstanding Performance
in a New Environment

Aerobord Ltd. Askeaton, Co. Limerick, Tel: 061 604600.
Aircell Ltd. Loch Gowna, Co. Cavan, Tel: 043 83550.

House B-210 Brick/Plaster Finish

House B-210 Stone/Plaster Finish

House B-210 Plaster Finish

House B-210 Tudor Finish

Plan Package Prices

Plan Type	Price	+VAT @ 21%	TOTAL
Section A (e.g. A-202)	€263.64	€55.36	**€319.00**
Section B	€288.43	€60.57	**€349.00**
Section C	€313.22	€65.78	**€379.00**
Section D	€338.02	€70.98	**€409.00**
Section E	€362.81	€76.19	**€439.00**

Prices shown are current at time of publication and include post and packaging worldwide. Allow up to ten working days for delivery of unaltered plans within Ireland upon receipt of payment.

There is no extra charge for mirroring the plans or altering the finish. In order to quote for further alterations log onto www.houseplans.ie or contact our office directly

We can also apply for planning permission on your behalf. Log onto www.houseplans.ie or contact our office directly

What You Receive

1. 7 copies of the plans with general dimensions at a scale of 1:100 for planning application/discussion purposes.

2. 5 copies of the fully dimensioned working drawing plans at a scale of 1:50 for building contractors/construction purposes. Drawings for Northern Ireland and Britain shall comply fully with local regulations.

3. 5 copies of the working written specification for builders pricing and construction purposes. Blank, user friendly copies are included in there for you to fill out as an alternative.

4. 7 copies of fully dimensioned garage plans as chosen, if required. If this is left blank on the order form, it is assumed that garage plans are not required. These may be used both for planning and construction

5. Two blank building contracts for you and your builder or sub-contractor.

We can supply extra copies when required.
Cost - €3 incl VAT for A1 drawings per sheet
Cost - €2 incl VAT for A2 drawings per sheet

Specification

The following shall allow us to accurately describe the materials to be used in your house.

If nothing is written, it is assumed that the choice shown in italic in the right hand column is satisfactory, (standard, but of good quality).

External Wall Construction: .... *Standard 300mm Cavity.*

Rainwater goods: .... *Seamless Aluminium*

Stairs: .... *Pine.*

Windows: .... *Double Glazed PVC as 3D Image.*

Skirting: .... *White Deal.*

Internal Doors:: .... *Six Panel Engineered Pine.*

Entrance Door:.. *Teak.*

Ground Floor Construction: .... *Concrete Slab*

Upper Floor Construction:.. *Suspended Timber*

Upper Floor Finish: .... *White Deal Floorboards*

Driveway: .... *Hardcore With Blinding*

Heating System:.. *Oil Fired Radiators*

Foulwater Drainage: .... *Standard Septic Tank/Percolation*

Water Supply: .... *Mains*

Garage:

Wall Construction:.. *9" block*

Wall Finish: .... *To match house*

Door: .... *To Clients Specification*

Windows: .... *Single Glazed PVC To Match House*

ADDITIONAL REMARKS

....

....

....

* A photocopy of this page is acceptable

Order Form

You may also phone Lo-Call 1890 713 713 or 00 353 56 7771300 to give the information below and order by credit card and/or with any queries.
Don't forget to include the specification on the previous page.
Log onto www.houseplans.ie or phone us to quote for alterations (in over 50% of cases there is no extra cost)

Name:.. Contact Telephone No:..

Home Address:...

....

Site Address (if applicable):..

....

PLAN NO. CHOSEN .... Mirror Plans: No   Yes

Wall Finish as shown on 3D image: Yes   No

If not, indicate finish to:

Front view: .... Side views:...

Rear view: ....

GARAGE NO. CHOSEN .... Mirror Plans: No   Yes

Wall finish/roof pitch to match main house: Yes   No

If not, indicate finish to:

Front view:... Side views:...

Rear view:...

Method of Payment: Cheque   Yes   No

Postal Order   Yes   No

Credit Card   Yes   No

If Credit Card then state: Card No.:...

Expiry Date:...

Signature:..

Fee attached *(See page 102 for plan prices.)*   €...

Send all details to: **MK HOME DESIGN LTD.,**
22 Upper Patrick Street, Kilkenny, Ireland.
or Fax to 056-7771300 (3 lines).

* A photocopy of this page is acceptable.